Desire and

Desire and Madness

An Anthology of Work

from

The Creative Writing Programme

at The University of Gloucestershire

2007

Edited by
Rebecca Nesvet and Nigel McLoughlin

Published by The Boho Press 2007

2 4 6 8 10 9 7 5 3 1

Copyright For This Anthology
© Rebecca Nesvet and Nigel McLoughlin 2007
All work contained within this anthology remains in the copyright of
the individual author

The contributors have asserted their right under the
Copyright, Designs and Patents Act 1988
to be identified as the author of their work

First published in Great Britain in 2007 by
The Boho Press
PO Box 109,
Portishead, Bristol. BS20 7ZJ

www.bohopress.co.uk

A CIP catalogue record for this book is available from the British
Library

ISBN 978-1-904781-99-8

Printed and bound in Great Britain by Biddles Ltd., King's Lynn, Norfolk

Contents

Novella

Rebecca Nesvet and Nigel McLoughlin

Introduction

But words came halting forth, wanting Invention's stay;
Invention, Nature's child, fled step-dame Study's blows;
And others' feet still seemed but strangers in my way.
Thus, great with child to speak, and helpless in my throes,
   Biting my truant pen, beating myself for spite—
   Fool, said my Muse to me, look in thy heart, and write.
Philip Sidney, circa 1579

There it is again: that familiar monster, the mad writer. As if the cliché needs any further exaggeration, he's driven mad by desire—or writer's block, which is a sort of desire. The elusive muse isn't listening, and won't until the desperate ascetic demonstrates his commitment to the craft by banging his head against the typewriter keys until blood streams from neat rows of bevel-edged square wounds. For Sidney, however, it's hopeless: the Remington company won't sell the first typewriter for another two hundred ninety-three years.

In the autumn of 2005, the students on a first-year fiction course at the University of Gloucestershire chose, as the communal theme for their final short-story submissions, 'Desire and Madness.' The topic provoked a wide range of writing, much of it exciting and extremely promising. Consequently, we decided to open out the challenge to all our students, and publish an anthology of the best writing on Desire and Madness. Being challengers to imposed boundaries, as all good writers are, some students submitted writing that did not proceed from the set theme, but engaged other dynamic and intriguing themes. We decided to publish some of those as well. After all, if we are to believe Philip Sidney, there is an integral link between writing and desire; and all writers are a bit mad. As a New Yorker cartoon of some years ago proclaimed, stockbrokers and investment bankers are workaholics: artists are obsessed.

All the fiction and poetry that you will read here was composed by students of the University of Gloucestershire, but that does not mean that writing, for these authors, is merely an academic activity. Most of our students arrive in their first term with notebooks or computer disks filled with writing that they have been working on for some time. Several, such as Penny Brinnen and Julie Frusher, had gained exposure for their work before they enrolled on the course. The anthology also includes some new voices, which we expect will sound increasingly familiar as they develop over the years.

Although writing can be painful—as Sidney testifies, its results should amuse, provoke, and engage. In the fiction pages of this anthology, you will find stories that fulfil all of those functions. Fans of science fiction will find the hard-boiled yet satirical futurism of Kayleigh Moore's 'Hatume' both humorous and chilling. Julie Frusher's 'Airhead' is a bittersweet foray into the fantasies of a strange and unpopular girl—fantasies that promise both liberation and destruction. Sonia Hendy-Isaac's 'Daddy Long Legs' is a spare, clear snapshot of one of those moments that is both commonplace and revelatory.

Harriet Hopkins' ekphrasm 'Existentialism on Massacre Night' is a reaction to the early modern painter Guido Reni's *Massacre of the Innocents*, a composition in which the massacre scene is problematically situated below the watchful eyes of a group of cherubim. Hopkins gives the angels modern voices, creating a decidedly uncanny effect. Amanda Evans' 'The Art of Evading the Question' is a witty, economical, and ironic burst of flash fiction. In an extract from work-in-progress "Hadi", Gemma Watters presents a confrontational modern retelling of Shakespeare's Hamlet and its long-debated subtexts. We look forward to reading the rest of this gritty, vivid piece, and we are certain that you will too.

The poetry presented here shows the range of what is being written by the students on the creative writing programme. Many have engaged fruitfully with traditional forms and experimented with them. Others have engaged with free verse to produce interesting and strong work. Many have explored the regions where these overlap. All those included have shown surprising maturity in their poetic voices. Penny

Brinnen uses the colloquial and the conversational well, the poems capture a particular voice and act as dramatic monologues in verse. Sally Darby's poems use assonances, consonances and dissonances to produce a pervasive musical quality to the work. Sometimes the language is pared down and lean; other times richly embroidered. Amanda Evans has an eye for the unusual viewpoint. The poems have a sensual richness and a wry humour that gives the verse an edgy feel. Julie Frusher's "Nocturne" is a study in psychological trauma and stream of consciousness. The juxtaposition of music and menace achieves the desired effect very well indeed. Harry Heywood has taken the sestina and reduced it to its elemental form – and the poem still works – a very deft trick. Ray McCrindle's verse has a delicacy about it. It is deeply felt without being sentimental and open enough to allow the reader's interpretation room in the poems. Rowan Middleton is a poet just hitting his stride: he has a real talent for controlled and sinuous verse that reacts well to the formal constraints he places upon it. Ian Morgan's poems have humour and tenderness that sometimes offset each other, and other times reinforce each other. His language has energy and he is willing to take risks in his work. Claire Opie's 'Gwithian' is a textured and taut prose poem. It plays off a romantic tradition but reenergises it for the modern era. Mariana Rueda Santana's Frustration takes an interesting and humourous view of the muses. Rueda Santana's work has a freshness of vision that allows the raw to mix with the wrought to produce an energetic verse.

Finally, Adam Palethorpe's acerbic novella *The Stripper's Tale*, printed here in its entirety, is a metafictional parcel of interlocking, competing stories. Palethorpe relates a tale about a stripper, a tale the stripper tells, and the larger story that is revealed when both these preceding layers are peeled away. As Palethorpe and his colleagues demonstrate, you don't need to drive yourself mad, with desire or otherwise, to write poetry or fiction. A better strategy is to simply find a good story. As the protagonist of *The Stripper's Tale* discovers, that can happen anywhere.

Rebecca Nesvet and Nigel McLoughlin

Prose

KAYLEIGH MOORE

Hatume

I hate this floating shit-hole, this rust bucket at the arse-end of nowhere. I hated it when the stench of recycled air first saturated my pores and singed my delicate nasal cavities, and I still hate it now three hours later. No wonder the last Chief up and nose-dived into the freezing vacuum of space, popping soundlessly thereupon. Now he's a pink cloud clinging to the gentle waves of the station's gravity and I'm left with this crap office and a pile of paperwork the size of my new desk.

I wish I had a window to see that spectacle when it cruises by, but I'm stuck in the goddamn bowels of this dive with only a barely functioning light to merrily illuminate the shitty grey floor and blue walls of my new universe. It's a commanding security position though, so I got what I wanted despite the location.

It was a long month getting here, and I swear I can still perceive the hum of the sub-engines at the bottom of my hearing. I docked in last night at Intrepid Station, orbiting some planet that's come out of the last big war needing a handup. It looked blistered and scorched past the lovingly outstretched docking limbs, the grey arms thrown out of the bottle-shaped body that had all the beauty of a bloated pig. My office is in the guts of it, nestled in the main habitat section, although 'habitat' does not cover this place.

It's not so old really, but neglect has cropped up everywhere with the fighting. Steam leaks randomly blast into corridors, there's a regular, disconcerting groan when something big breaks in the core, and if the lights manage to stay constant for an hour it's a triumph. I can tell this office used to be sleek, clean and modern, but now the rounded walls are stained, the sensually styled furniture battered and faded, and the one-way glass panels that comprise my sliding doors are scratched up like some run-down peep-show booth. It's hard to believe that this is the Planetary Security Office, but my unremitting cynicism is making the transition of expectations easier.

It seems everything is put on a sliding scale during war, and when in the last hundred years haven't we been at war with someone? Sometimes I really despise the arrogance of my own damned species,

13

particularly for roping in so many other poor schmucks to take on the big bad, who probably isn't that bad anyway. All my new subordinates are rather begrudging of humanity and its acquired strength as well. I don't need to look up at the face of the officer before me to know that. As one of only two humans in this place, I knew I wasn't going to be welcomed. It doesn't help that the other guy was taken in for first-degree murder yesterday, only further helping to soil our species' reputation. Selfish bastard. It was probably this one who took him in, which is just peachy.

'Commander Hatume?' He's tall, azure-skinned and has been standing there for several minutes now. I believe his name is Dietz, if I remember correctly from the station-logs I read coming over here. The maroon uniform is obviously tailored to fit every muscled curve and anything that could possible shine has been polished to a fault. I can see my distorted reflection a thousand times over, and to finish it all he's posturing and speaking as if he's part of the Galactic Royal Guard. So far, I've been ignoring this pompous idiot to let him deflate to more tolerable levels of fastidiousness.

I tap the remains of my cigarette into the corner of the desk, watching the task intently. He holds his breath and quickly assesses the situation, finally cottoning on that I'm not going to be playing his haughtily civilised little game. I think it's always best to establish that early, so people know what they've been lumped with until one of us dies or gets shipped out. It's not like they didn't know what they were getting when my papers went out. My last three disciplinary reports had the word 'psychotic' in them, more than once. It's not hard to see why my seniors wanted shot of me with as great a distance applied as possible. So here I am on the outskirts of the Friendly Border, 'friendly' an optimistic label here. I grind my cigarette harder as I attempt to recall the last meeting I had anywhere near Earth and find myself reaching back years.

When I'm quite done I look across to my potential lodger. standing squat and frightened at Dietz's side. He's short and mole-like, with muddy brown skin and grooves I could loose my fingers in. Scraps of fabric drape about him creating a shapeless lump, and he quivers with every breath. He continues to meet my gaze throughout my stare. Between the two of them, I like him better.

Raising an inviting eyebrow to Dietz, I gesture vaguely for him to speak. He clears his throat and nudges at the elbow of his prisoner, making the wrinkly thingy shudder and gnash its jaws. 'Commander Hatume, this… creature was found breaking and entering down in the recycling centre.'

My head tips to one side, considering, and as I fold my arms I see Dietz glancing furtively as my breasts converge. I smirk and briefly tense my biceps, giving them and him a little jolt. His ears darken and I begin a mental scoreboard for us. Currently I'm winning. 'Put him in Cell Three and I'll deal with him in a minute.'

His babyish eyes widen and he looks between the prisoner and myself. 'But, Commander Hatume—'

'Wants you to leave now. Put him in Cell Three and piss off,' I reiterate firmly. Protocol dictates that I'm not alone with any prisoner out of a cell, but I want a smoke, and I've never had more trouble than I can manage.

Dietz shuffles a bit, his pigeon chest finally deflating. I imagine I can hear that satisfying little hiss out of his rectum as those proud glands empty. Stupid bloody species. He nods a little though, his hand detaching from mole-man and surreptitiously rubbing against his thigh before dropping to his side. There's a dark patch from the grease left, and with a smile I know that that stain won't come out easy.

He leads the smaller alien through a door to the right and I hear the security field crackle to life. Moments later, he's back out and straight through my doors without a glance, head high and heels clicking sharply on the metal floor.

Deciding that I can leave the prisoner to stew for a few minutes, I regard the dryer in the corner of my office. It isn't done yet, and despite my agitation I resolve to let it finish. Soggy smokes disagree with me anyway. My lungs and throat don't mind the biological tar but my lips go purple when it leaks. It'll also give the rodent in the cage under my desk time to recover. It's on its last legs and I expect it'll die in the next few weeks. It's deaf, dumb, blind and happy, but it's not bleeding off as well as it used to. The sickly-smooth taste of its blood is starting to curdle too. Best order in some more later.

That's something I miss about the old fags: their reliability. Every time, you're guaranteed a dry, rich whisper that buzzes your brain and tickles your lungs. With these smokes though, it's a game of roulette with their taste and kick. There's also the fact that you have to cook one up each time yourself. It used to be purchase, open and smoke,

15

but now there's the tedious extraction and drying process. That is unless you can afford a supplier. Funny guys them, surrounded by confetti cages of fuzz-balls and high on the fumes.

The whole breed got modded about eight years ago, initially to make the perfect pet. They became brightly-coloured little things that couldn't feel pain because of a geneticist with a God-complex who saw fit to tweak with their nerve endings. Now their blood's a red cocktail of genetic chemistry and tipsy chemicals, and they float through their short lives on a perpetual self-drugged high. With reliable, dry cigarettes banned at the same time as all this, addicts were going to put two and two together and have a go. And bless the little sod who was good enough to experiment with Mr. Whiskers' narcotic goods whilst his little girl was out at pre-school.

Every smoke is a little bit different, the sweetly acidic taste always somewhere else in the vast sundry range. Thanks to all the genetic jiggling there are so many reactions going on in their tiny bodies at once that they are invariably different animals every time you begin the lengthy process.

My own lime-coloured creature stumbles into its wheel for the third time in the last five minutes, rapidly blinking over empty eye-sockets. Its eyes glowed in the dark and it rarely blinked, and with this office effectively only lit by the computer screen, that had offended me. So an hour ago, out they came and off it happily squeaked and I rolled up a fresh one from the stuff that came out of the needle.

The dryer finally begins smoking coppery clouds, and I get up to knock off the switch. I scrape the crusted flakes off the heated plate with my shiny new ID card and into my palm, then fumble around in my thigh pocket for a bit of paper. Ten seconds later I'm feeling a bit brighter, the itch of the craving finally abated.

Toxins nip into and about my bloodstream. I give them a few seconds to really get going before pulling my ponytail tighter, having decided to play with being professional for a few minutes, or until I get bored. I consider dragging my chair into the cell room but see that it's affixed. The little chair opposite the desk is bolted down too. Obviously less stuff to throw around if someone gets into a tantrum, or else someone read my record before I got here.

Fresh cigarette between a canine and a premolar, I make my way into the cell room and stand before my latest guest, Datapad in hand to take down the details. I've got him facing Cell Five where my first catch of the day lies in a crumpled heap. I believe he makes a good visual deterrent. I've got it down in the report as a result of 'violently resisting arrest'.

'Name?' I ask around my smoke, tonguing the filter and savouring the taste.

'Crint. Eyon Crint.' His voice is rough but timid, lips making loud smacking sounds as he gets the words out. He hasn't moved from the narrow bench. He wrings his wrinkled hands so hard that they smooth and bunch alternately.

I jot down the name and bring up his file, familiarising myself with it for a moment. With a grunt I drop it to my side and key-card the security field, watching the yellow sparks suddenly blink out. Crint seems to shrink in on himself as I enter. I sit a distance away on the bench and cross my legs.

'I'm going to let you go, Crint.' He relaxes but maintains an air of suspicion. 'I've read up on you before. I know you've got a wife and seven kids, and I know you work down in waste disposal and don't make much. I also know that your father died recently and that he'd been sending you money to help out. Finally, I know that you've been in here more than once for petty crimes.'

Crint nods silently, his head rolling around on the folds of his neck. The smell is amazing. I suck hard on the cigarette again, exhaling through my nose. 'I think you were down in recycling trying to break something – 'cause there's nothing worth stealing. Then you'd get the overtime to repair it between everything else that's going on here, and it's all breaking down all the time anyway so who would notice?'

He shuffles awkwardly on the bench, rubbing his greasiness into the wall panels. 'It wasn't gonna be anyt'in' really bad.'

'Well that's something at least, and I'll let you off with a warning.' I stand with a thin smile and he follows suit, stepping out of the cell with me. 'Now, there's a big benefits system that can help you out, and I don't think you're getting all you can out of it. It's an easy system to work, so go sort that out and keep out of trouble, and then we won't have to meet like this again.'

Grateful, Crint nods repeatedly and offers a hand. I glance at the gleaming flesh and shake my head with a grimace, taking the last of my cigarette from my lips. He seems to be used to that and puts it back in his pocket with a smile.

After seeing him out of the office I jot some crap about the 'incident' on the Datapad and throw it into my top drawer. I dump the smouldering remains of my cigarette on the floor and stamp a boot on it before slipping both feet neatly under my chair. Two figures move across the main doors before they open smoothly, and I see that my favourite officer has returned with a skinny young lad in his grip. He looks exceptionally pleased to see me. Well, exceptionally something, anyway.

The itch of a craving starts up again.

JULIE FRUSHER

Airhead

'Susan, Susan, who are you talking to?'

The young girl jumped away from the window as her mother entered the bedroom.

'No-one,' Susan quietly replied, her face reddening. She could never tell lies.

Her mother's face softened and she gently reached out to push a stray lock of blonde hair out of Susan's face. 'Aren't you a bit old for that invisible friend of yours?'

Susan didn't answer. Her mother would never understand the voice in her head; the one that spoke so seductively about the kingdom beyond the sea, where the only inhabitants were the seagulls whose wide wings rose and fell with the whim of the air currents. A place where there were no people; no one to tease or bully her or make her life such a complete misery.

Her mother shook her head, not knowing how to breach the unseen wall that had recently grown between her and her daughter. She had given up trying to fathom what was going on. Surely it was just a phase and Susan would soon grow out of it.

'Come on, love,' she said, 'you'd better get a move on or else you'll be late for school.' With one last look over her shoulder, her mother closed the bedroom door and walked away.

Susan looked out of the window again, pressing her fingers and nose against the cold glass. The seagulls were still playing on the wind, their white wings standing out starkly against the storm clouds heading in from the south. Then a movement below the window made her look down. It was the five from her class, three girls and two boys. They were passing in the street beneath her window, laughing and joking amongst themselves, as they always did. Even when they were holding her down and stealing whatever she had in her pockets. One of them looked up and pointed.

'There's Airhead!' she shouted.

'Hey, Airhead, coming down to play or are you too busy being a bird? Squawk! Squawk! SQUAWK!'

'You'd better hurry up and get to school and make sure you bring some money!'

Closing her eyes, she once again felt that familiar fear beginning in the pit of her stomach, like snakes coiling and uncoiling in the labyrinth of her insides. She was about to turn away from the window when she noticed that they had lost all interest in her. An older boy was with them, handing out small packages of something. She had seen him before, hanging around the school, but she hadn't really taken much notice of him, nor he of her.

Within moments they had disappeared from her view, further down the street. She had been forgotten now that the older boy had turned up. Picking up her school bag, she walked out of the bedroom and down the stairs. Her mother called goodbye to her as she heard the click of the front door latch and Susan mumbled something in reply. But she didn't really know what. She hoisted the bag onto her shoulder and left the safety of the house, her gaze directed at the pavement. She had to concentrate; put one foot after the other in a determined act of will so that she wouldn't run back home. Reaching the end of the road, she stopped. Instead of turning left for school, she turned right, heading for the cliffs. It looked as if it might rain later, and she didn't have her coat, but she didn't care. At least at the cliffs she'd feel safe.

Her morning was spent sat on a bench looking out to sea. The cold wind whipped her hair across her face and every now and again a few spots of rain – or was it sea spray? – moistened her face. But although she shivered at the chill under her skin, she did not move. She was transfixed by the turbulent rolling of the grey ocean, by its cold, steely vastness. Seagulls floated effortlessly over her head, calling to each other, sharing their stories. She closed her eyes, and imagined, as she always did, what it felt like to float so freely.

'Susan, Susan,' came the voice in her head. It always came to her when she was thinking of the sea. 'Are you watching my beloved birds?'

Susan nodded, a smile spreading across her face. She felt safe, now that He was here.

'Are you still mine, Susan?' he asked.

'Yes, oh yes,' cried Susan to the wind. 'Let me be with you. Tell me how I can be with you.'

'Have patience. You are not of the air, child. Your body is still of the earth. We can only meet like this for now...' The voice was soft and had the sound of summer oceans, far off exotic beaches.

'But I want to be with you,' Susan repeated. 'I'll do anything, anything...'

'Be patient, Susan, keep the faith...' The words started to melt away into the air, dispersing around her like grains of sand in a storm.

'No, come back,' she shouted, and reached out as if to try and pluck the fading voice back from where she couldn't follow. All she felt was the damp, biting wind rushing through her fingers. And she couldn't catch the wind. No one could. A seagull settled a few metres away on the edge of the cliff and gave a mournful, mocking cry before taking off again and hovering in the wind.

Susan slumped back into the seat, lost once more in a world of self-pity. The rest of the gulls had moved further out to sea now, as if she was now excluded from their company.

'They're so free aren't they?' said a soft voice beside her.

She jumped and looked round. The older boy she had seen earlier with the others was sitting next to her. She hadn't heard him approach. His eyes were seaweed green. His hair was long, wind-brushed.

'W...what?' she said, suddenly unsure of this conversation. In fact, wondering whether she should be talking to a stranger at all.

'The seagulls. They're so free, like they're dancing. I like to watch them too.'

His voice was warm and somehow familiar, with an Irish lilt. It reminded her of ... safety. The resentment disappeared and she managed a smile.

'I ... I sometimes close my eyes and feel that I *am* one. I imagine that I can fly over the sea, far away from here.'

There. She'd said it. The words she had never said to anyone else. And to a stranger. But somehow she didn't feel like he was a stranger; she felt like she knew him well. Had known him for centuries.'

He smiled. Smiled, not laughed. She had told him her deepest shame and he hadn't made fun of her.

'Maybe you will someday, Susan,' he said.

She caught her breath. He knew her name. How could he know her name? Unless ... Her mind worked fast, coming to the only conclusion that made any sense, the only conclusion she wanted to think about.

'You're Him, aren't you? You've come to take me there?'

The boy frowned for a moment, puzzled, then his expression changed. 'Perhaps I am,' he said quietly. 'Perhaps I am Him.'

'I've been waiting, you know. I knew you'd come eventually.'

'So, tell me now, what is it you want? Maybe I can grant your wish.' He smiled, reached out and tucked a wisp of Susan's rat-tailed hair behind her ear.

Eyes wide, Susan touched where he had touched. Maybe it was imagination but her hair felt warm, golden.

She thought she heard a suppressed laugh from behind one of the bushes but she ignored it. So what if they had followed her? They couldn't hurt her now. He was here and would protect her. She'd show them.

'Will you make me fly?' she asked, grabbing hold of his arm. It was solid. It felt human.

He grinned. 'Fly? That's the one thing I can make you do easily enough. Are you sure, though?'

'It's all I've ever wanted, to be up there with them.'

He followed her pointing finger out to sea where the birds seemed to hover in anticipation.

He shrugged. 'OK, but it'll cost you.'

'Cost?' she asked, suddenly bewildered.

'You don't think these things come for free, do you? Everything has a price Susan and mine is two quid, just for you.'

'But ... but,' she faltered. Something didn't quite fit. Perhaps it was a test. He was testing her resolve – perhaps the endless waiting was not enough.

Her hesitation seemed to annoy him. 'Come on, I haven't got all day.'

His words drove away her caution. Of course he hadn't got all day. It must have taken every bit of his energy to change into a human from his spirit form. 'Yes, I want to fly. Here ...' she dug into her coat pocket and fished out two pound coins – her dinner money ... 'have this.'

He closed his fist around the money and pulled a paper bag from inside his jacket. Tearing what looked like a small transfer from a thin roll, he passed it to her.

'What's this?'

'This is the magic that will make you fly. Just put it in your mouth and soon you'll be up with them.'

'And with you?'

He shrugged, disinterested now his business was done. 'Whatever.'

She put the funny transfer thing in her mouth, as he'd said. Turning back again, she found that he'd gone. Disappeared. Well, of course. He would be waiting for her.

At first nothing happened. She was puzzled. Was it possible that he'd lied? Then, slowly, she began to feel lighter, free-er. Colours and shapes changed. Chaos collided in her head and drew beautiful patterns. She extended her arms and felt them change into wings – multi-coloured wings.

'Susan,' called the voice in her head. 'Are you watching my beloved birds?'

'Susan,' called other voices, voices that weren't in her head. She turned to see the others, her tormentors, standing a small way away. She tried to flap her wings, to take off and soar above them but they obviously weren't strong enough yet. She stayed grounded. The children were laughing, each sound rolling out of their mouths and swirling like blue mist. The mist started to come for her, rolling in like a sea fog. She knew that if she stayed she would be lost forever. Their bodies began to turn into sea-snakes, twisting and curling as they drew nearer.

She heard the voice at her side again. Or was it the older boy? She couldn't tell. 'Go on, Susan, time to fly. If you go now, they cannot hurt you.'

With one backwards look, she ran for the cliff edge and for a moment stood there, arms outstretched, eyes towards the distant horizon. There was a screaming noise in the distance and then she launched herself from the ledge. In her mind she floated upwards, away from the earth, to that place where sea becomes sky and sky becomes sea. She couldn't remember a time when she had been happier than this.

'You're mine now,' said the voice, 'just like all the rest,' and then she was swooping towards the waiting arms of the jagged rocks, laughing.

Up on the cliff top a small group of children and an older boy stood, their eyes and mouths perfect circles of disbelief. In the sky above them seagulls rose and fell with the whims of the air currents, sharing their stories.

SONIA HENDY-ISAAC

Daddy Long-Legs

'Why are women so scared of them?' he asked, barely disguising his contempt.

'They've got too many legs,' she muttered to his back, drawing her own bare legs to her chest as if the foetal position would save her. 'Did you know that if they could penetrate human skin they'd be the most venomous insect in the country?' She knew he wouldn't know, but would pretend to.

'Don't be ridiculous.'

His retort was less than effective, as he backed away from trying to catch it. 'Really? Are you winding me up?'

He turned to meet her stare and watched her pull herself further into the sofa. Her arms wrapped around her knees; her breasts pressed into a pleasing cleavage.

'It's late. If I had the energy to wind you up it wouldn't be over that bloody thing.' She felt the tightness in her neck and realised the evening had done little to relieve it.

'Are you going to catch it or shall I swipe it with the paper?'

'You can't just go around killing things.' He watched it fly back and forth across the window frame.

'It's in my space and I don't like it – get it out or I'll kill it. I hate the thought of it flying about when I'm sleeping.' She unfolded herself, reached for a cigarette and lit it.

'Thought you didn't smoke in the house?'

'It's my house, I do as I please. Can you get it out or not?'

'Get me a jar or something to catch it in, and some card to put on the top.'

'Jeez! If I realised it was such a bloody hassle I'd have killed it when you left!' She blew the smoke out angrily, and avoided his eye.

'Do you want me to go, then?' He knew that he should, but he wanted another chance. She ignored the question: it stank of rhetoric.

'Do you want coffee?' She realised that that question wasn't appropriate either, given the circumstances.

Reaching for the throw from the back of the sofa, she draped it around her shoulders and thought of the foil capes they wrap around marathon runners when they cross the line. She pictured the look of delight on their faces when they had achieved their goal. She stubbed out her half-smoked cigarette in the make shift ashtray.

He watched her sashay barefoot across the stone floor and heard the water hit the steel sink before the kettle gave it a softer reception. He looked down at the borrowed dressing gown and smelt her on the collar. He couldn't remember exactly how it had happened. He'd collected her at seven with a bunch of yellow roses. She had kissed him firmly before placing them in water. The meal had been good; they had shared each other's food. He'd felt surprisingly relaxed, despite only one glass of wine and had started talking about his father. The kettle started to rumble next door.

She placed the red china mugs next to each other and realised she didn't even know how he had his coffee. Staring at the roses she felt unsure about him now – it had all been going so well. Hours spent in effortless conversation, it could have been something. If she were honest she'd felt nervous when he started talking about his father. He sounded like a cruel bastard who only adopted to appease his own conscience and his family obsessed wife. It spooked her when he confessed he'd never told anyone about what he had endured – not even his ex-wife apparently. It was either a line to get her into bed or the truth. Either way she felt uncomfortable with it.

He followed her into the kitchen and tried to rub her shoulders beneath the woollen throw.

'Do you take milk?' she asked, moving towards the fridge.

'No thanks, as it comes. Did you find an empty jar?' He gazed around the clinical steel kitchen. It looked empty. She handed him the mug of steaming instant coffee and returned to the sofa gripping the tartan throw with one hand, coffee cup in the other.

'No, look, don't worry about it. I'll sort it out later.'

As he stood in the doorframe she noticed that the dressing gown barely covered him, but was thankfully neutral white. She tried to settle back into the sofa but couldn't.

'Look, about earlier, it's never happened like that before. I don't know what to make of it …' He moved toward her. The silence in the space between them deafened her.

'I don't need a post-mortem right now – it happened, it was probably the wine.'

It was his turn to feign deafness. 'You were just so full on.'

She placed the coffee next to her cigarettes and gripped the throw tighter to her chest. 'I think it's time you left.'

'Don't be like that, it was just a bit surprising that's all.'

'Yes, for me too! Although not exactly in the way I'd hoped!' Sarcasm and anger laced her voice in equal measure now. 'Just get out and take your fucking excuses with you!'

He attempted to explain, to apologise, but pride called him to task.

'Fine, I'll call you tomorrow when you've had a chance to calm down.' He snatched his keys from the table and slopped his coffee cup in their place, then realised that the grand exit was incomplete without his clothes. He gazed up at the glass staircase and bitterly regretted not getting dressed straight away. 'I'll get my clothes and go then.'

Her face was flushed. He avoided her glare as he walked past her to the stairs. As he reached the top, he sprang from the sofa and returned to the kitchen. Whilst pouring herself a whiskey she listened to him moving in the room above her. She downed the amber fluid and as the warmth of it filled her she let the throw slip from her body to the floor. She followed him up. They met on the landing but she sidestepped into the open bathroom to let him pass without the need for contact.

'I'll call you, yes?' He glanced at her nakedness.

'I'm tired. I'm going to shower and get some sleep. Just pull the door to when you go. Night.'

She closed the bathroom door and he heard the bolt land home. He had run out of things to say. As he descended the stairs he heard the shower's crescendo. Grabbing a final sip of his coffee he noticed yesterday's newspaper folded on the table, the remains of the daddy long legs crumpled on its back page.

HARRIET HOPKINS

Existentialism on Massacre Night

After Guido Reni's painting 'The Massacre of the Innocents'

The two small ones hid out of the way, above the commotion.
They viewed the scene from an objective point of view. This point of
view was so objective, in fact, that they didn't really think what was
happening was all that terrible anyway – they had seen *far* worse.
Currently, they were busy discussing the ratings of a new show being
performed nightly back in 'The Great Land', and wondering whether
Gabriel had *painted* his wings purple, or if it was just one of his many
gifts due to his status as one of the higher choirs.

A spurt of blood flew up and narrowly missed Agatha, who bolted
to the right with a swift motion of the hips, almost forcing her off the
perch.

'Watch it!' she shouted at the oblivious crowd below.

'Ooh, are you a'right?' Maureen crooned in her heavy Welsh
accent – she had chosen this for the hilarity of it all, and its ability to
grate at quite a few people.

'Only just, Reen. Only bloody just!'

Agatha, thinking the idea such a great one, had followed in her
friends footsteps, taking the accent and presenting it with huge
amounts of gusto.

'No consideration them lot, 'ave they?'

'Well, look at the way they treat each other, Reen. Can't expect
anymore respect just because we're a higher being now, can we?'

'What them girlies need is a leader. Someone who'll tell them they
don't need to stand for it, that 'er upstairs doesn't stand for it either,
and punishes 'em all duly!'

'You're still adamant he's a girl 'en?'

'Woman, Agatha. Woman!'

'Oh, right.' Agatha rolled her eyes inconspicuously. 'Woman,
then.'

'Thank you. And, yes. In fact, I *know* he's a...*she's* a woman.'

'But *how* do you know? I mean, you've never met him...sorry,
her...'ave you?'

'Well, not in so many words, no, but...'

'Not in *any* words, Reen! You're not permitted inside the Big building, same as the rest of us.'

'Well, no, I know that Ag, but I saw...'

'What? What did you see?'

'Well...and don't laugh now Ag, but...I thought I saw a...' Maureen dropped her voice to a low whisper, out of pure embarrassment far more than secrecy, 'a reflection.'

'Oh, Reen!!' Agatha crowed, beside herself with disbelief. 'I've heard some stories in my time, but never one so ridiculous as that!'

'Oh, bugger you, Agatha Green!'

Agatha was now unable to contain her laughter, and proceeded to roll about on the perch, her small feathers flapping furiously against the air. Of course, it was about that time that one of the men from below began to rip the small, brown haired, dying woman's skirt and undergarments off, and continued to rape her. The screams of the girl echoed so far around the room that they even struck a chord with Maureen and Agatha. The two fell silent.

'Oh, I can't stand this anymore, y'know. Surely there's something more we can do about it?'

'I know how you feel, Aggy, honestly I do. But it's not up to us, is it? It's 'er upstairs. She doles out the powers and the rights to use them, and we're just here to...follow orders.'

'You mean we're just here to look pretty.'

'Oh, Agatha!'

'Well, what else are we here for?'

'To...watch over and...give comfort.'

'I don't see any of them girls and babies looking comforted, do you?!'

'Well...'

'Well, nothing, Maureen! There's no sense in it! I don't even know if I believe in any of it anymore. Could be anything. Could be a conspiracy. How would we know? We're not even allowed to see 'her', how can we really know it's the truth we're gettin'?'

'What are you getting at here, Ag?'

'Well...I mean...what rightful 'God' would allow such torture to go on? What being would be happy enough to stand back and let these things happen?'

'*Agatha*! I'm astounded! Existentialism at this time of night? What's gotten into you?!'

'This, Reeny! This!' Agatha expostulated, gesticulating towards the din below. A young girl was desperately trying to escape, her baby clutched tightly in her arms, but was pounded on by three brutal, heavily armed men, before she had any real chance.

'Oh, but there's nothing anyone can do about that Agatha, not even God Herself!'

'But why not? If 'she' can create the whole universe, split the red sea for Moses, bring down a flood that wipes out the whole world's population, why can't he…she…stop something as small as this?'

'Well, because…because it's not in the pattern of things, is it? This has to happen. It's all part of her big plan.'

'Well, buggery to her big plan. I think it's crap!'

'You can't say that!'

'I just did!'

'But we don't have freedom of choice like them, Ag. We're not allowed!'

'Who says?'

'Well…um…'

'See! It was just a rumour that's caught on like wildfire, and now everybody sticks to it because they're too afraid to step out of line, just in case. You don't see me being struck down by a great bolt of lightning, do you?'

The two looked up to the skies for a moment, and contemplated the clouds. White and fluffy, just like they had been before.

'Well,' Reeny started sulkily, 'no…but…'

'But what?'

'Just that…'

'What?'

'Nothing.'

A silence loomed over the two as Reeny sulked at her own incapability to give a good argument, and Agatha thought more about why God let all these things happen. She got more and more agitated and annoyed at life, and what many people, angels, spirits and more had to go through before receiving a divine sense of peace. She apparently hadn't been through enough yet. But then she didn't know if cherubs had an…end. They might just go on forever, witnessing atrocities like this. But then she didn't know either how long the world, as in Earth, would go on for anyway. And once that was gone…what would her job be then?

'There goes another one.' Reeny sighed, dropping the straw she was holding down onto the ground.

'How many's that now?' Agatha asked, yawning as she pulled the cloud closer around her stomach.

'Fourteen, not including the mothers. One almost got away, but that ruffian over there grabbed her by the hair and stabbed her in the back of the neck.'

'Oof!' Agatha's cringe was almost painful itself. She hated unfair practise. 'What a bastard!'

The two cherubs paused to watch the blue-shirted man tread on a baby's body just to make perfectly sure it was dead – there was only one left alive now, and the men took great pleasure in taunting the woman who was holding her dead baby close in her arms.

'Reckon they'll all do 'er before they kill her?'

'I would imagine so Reeny, I would imagine so.'

'Why do they do that, d'you think?'

'Well, sometimes it's pure hormonal urge, or arrogance. Of course, some do it because they feel…well…inadequate.'

'What d'you mean inadequate?'

Agatha didn't answer straight away. She was trying to find the right words – the polite words.

'Well, it's like they're compensating for something.'

'For what?'

'Well, down there, y'know.'

'Down where?'

'There!' Agatha was madly trying to inform Maureen with slight movements of her head, eyes, and a tight lipped expression.

'Agatha, just tell me!'

'They've got little willies!' Reeny looked mortified. So did the men who were surrounding the young woman on the ground. They looked up to the cloud upon which Agatha and Maureen had perched, but they had already gone.

AMANDA EVANS

The Art of Evading the Question.

'Anyways I was finking of getting her that poster, so annoying that they sold out!' Daniel jokingly slammed his fist on the restaurant's pitted Formica tabletop in disappointment and grinned at Erin, but as her head was bowed she missed it.

She paused for a moment in absently blowing down the straw into her coke to reply. 'Yeah.'

'I wish I had the 'net, then I could get it there.' Erin kept her dark head bowed and mumbled something as non-committal as possible. There was an awkward pause (which she relished), before he cleared his throat and continued hesitantly. 'Uh... I don't suppose you'd get it for me if I gave you the money to put into your account?'

The cardboard cup cradled in her hands took on a decidedly less cyclindrical shape as her fingers tightened around it. Then she looked up, her 'happy face' firmly in place, and rolled her eyes. 'Sure, but I need the money soon, I haven't got much as it is.' She winced inwardly as he squealed and hugged her.

'Thanks so much, Erin, love you!'

If only. All he ever thought about was 'Her'. Fern. Erin didn't understand it. OK, so she was no stunner, but she was as good a friend as his crush and they spent more time together, knew more about each other, shared at least *one* common interest. More than could be said for Fern and him. Fern wasn't even interested in him as potential boyfriend material. She had in fact commented that he was about as far from claiming the position as it was possible to be. But for some reason, Daniel refused to acknowledge this, and continued to hound her with a single-mindedness that was impressive, yet pathetic.

Incidentally, pathetic was exactly how Erin felt, skulking around in the background watching Daniel obsess over her best friend for the better part of a year, hoping, though she knew it was wrong, that Fern would just finally reject him in a way not even Mr. Optimist himself could mistake. She'd tried prodding Fern in that direction before, urging her to put him out of his misery, under the guise of a friend concerned for both of them. But her best friend was just too sensitive to Daniel's feelings, and refused to let him down, no matter how gently. Erin had felt so selfish and manipulative then, and she still felt the familiar twinge of guilt now as she regarded Daniel gazing dreamily into space.

Why couldn't he just *see* what was directly in front of him? Their mutual friends all knew about his pursuit of the inaccessible Fern, and had commented more than once that he would be wise to accept she wasn't interested. But Daniel had never been a master of the detection of subtlety. The only way he would believe that he hadn't a chance with Fern would be if she herself told him, in no uncertain terms, to bugger off and stop harassing her. Even then, it would probably take reiterating.

It wasn't fair. She was doomed to be no more than a 'good mate' forever. A small sigh escaped her. She reached for a paper napkin and began to fold it randomly.

'What's up?' Typical. Daniel always noticed when she was even the slightest bit miserable. Irritating, really, considering his total oblivion when it came to other, glaringly obvious, things.

'Nothing.' The flimsy square of paper in her hands began to resolve itself into something resembling a boat.

She watched through her eyelashes as he unconsciously picked up a napkin and copied her movements. 'Then why're you sighing?'

'I don't wanna talk about it.' She threw her creation down on the red plastic tray on the table between them.

He scrutinised her for a long moment, before looking away as the door to the restaurant opened behind him. She shot him a dark glare that would have melted his head had she been possessed of any kind of super-power. His head, intact, swung back round to her and she dropped her gaze to her fingers as they now fiddled with the paper packaging of a drinking straw.

She began inventing some previously undiscovered form of origami as he responded. 'Fine, I was only asking, Jeez.' He fell silent, much to her relief, but it was short lived. 'Why do you always do this?' He was irritable, something it wasn't often his wont to be, it usually took a great deal of proverbial button-pushing to faze him. She wondered that he had risen to her bait so quickly, but soon dismissed it, she had been in near perpetual bad mood recently that would have annoyed a saint.

She gave up trying to maintain her pleasant expression, letting her features drop into a small, annoyed frown. 'What?'

'Go all depressed and sigh like you want me to notice or summat, and then say it's nuffin'? It's obviously not nuffin' or you wouldn't be sitting there with your face tripping you.' He was always *so* eloquent. His napkin was now in shreds. It joined her boat-shaped piece of tissue on the tray.

Suddenly she was furious with herself. She grabbed her bag from the chair next to her and stood up, Coke in hand. 'You done?' she asked, not waiting for an answer as she moved away.

He nodded nonetheless, and stood. They carried their empty burger and chip wrappers to the bin. A rather skinny origami crane accompanied them in. He followed her out of the door she held open for him. He didn't believe in male gallantry and all that crap, which she supposed was fair enough. Daniel didn't reiterate his question, which was just as well, as she had no inclination to answer it.

GEMMA WATTERS

Hadi

The yellow stained tip of Hadi's index finger landed on the pink pill. On it was an engraved picture of a dove. Well, it looked like a dove, that's what Steve had told him, but it was so small it could have been anything. Hadi picked up his glass of sparkling mineral water, with a wedge of lime, and held the pill between his thumb and forefinger. He rolled it gently back and forth. His blood was thumping from his toes, to his thighs and up to his head. A hundred fists seemed to be striking Hadi's arms from inside his veins. He dropped the pink pill into his gaping mouth and swiftly poured some water down his throat. He tasted the bitterness, as the pill sizzled and disintegrated. The chemicals raced through his body, entering the bloodstream, like a tidal wave.

Only seconds after he consumed the pill, there was a heavy knock at the door. Someone was shaking the gold handle. It was disturbing his moment quite viciously.

'Hadi... open the door, please. I...I...g.. got somethin' to tell ya'.' The woman's voice was trying to sound stable.

'Hadi, damn it! Please, open the door.' Her words seemed more focused the second time. Hadi brushed the remaining pills, with his hand, into a silver tobacco tin. The tin housed many other similar looking pills. He tightly closed its lid, and pushed it under the teal cushion of his chair. He turned his music down and walked over to unlock the door, to unwelcome in, his crying mother.

'What do you want? I'm going out.' Hadi's mother tripped over her feet as she crossed the threshold from the hallway and into her son's bedroom.

Hadi's bedroom resembled the interior of a Moroccan casbah. It was a large square room with deep purple painted walls. In the centre was an imposing bed, with four immense hand-carved wooden posts. made from maple. In the far corner of the room, a plastic pod like chair was hanging from the ceiling. Hadi stomped his feet across his nearly black carpet and sat on the pod. He could feel the metal tin underneath the fat, not that there was much, of his ass. His mother took a seat on the corner of his bed. 'Riders on the Storm' whispered from the stereo speakers. '*...killer on the road. Well you gotta love your man. Take him by the hand. Make him understand.*'

Several minutes passed with no spoken words. Geri's eyes appeared to be looking straight through Hadi, as if he had an open hole in his head. He tapped his foot against the side of the black coffee table. Geri's eyes looked as if she had just dabbed them with acid.

'Mom, if you just came in here to feel sorry for yourself then you can go now.'

'I... I'm not drunk, Hadi. Trust me. Come over here and smell my breath.'

'I'm not going to smell your breath, mom.'

'Damn it, Hadi!' Geri strode over to her son. Her right knee gave way and she stumbled slightly. She grabbed Hadi's arm. She didn't grab it fiercely though, she lightly clenched it. She drew in a deep breath and slowly released a gentle breeze that pleasantly greeted his cheeks. It was true. He couldn't smell his mother's usual Coors' breath. She gave her son a gentle kiss on the lips and released her touch from his arm. She went back to her corner on the bed.

*　　*　　*

So, anyway, that's how she told me. On a Friday night after I had just swallowed an ecstasy pill. It kind of surpassed me though, you know, the whole shock factor. As my mom sat there talking and talking, it was as though I couldn't hear anything. I seemed to have leapt into a TV. I was now the star of a silent, black and white movie.

The pill, halfway through our hour-long meeting, began to possess my feelings. I reached for my sofa cushion and placed it conspicuously on my lap. I was hoping to distract my mom, from the visible signs of my drug-induced euphoria. I sat there fiddling with the zip of the cushion. The large purple walls of my room began to move. I had never before noticed the paper lining, behind the paint. Swirls were moving across the walls, like mini Catherine Wheels. My eyes couldn't take the movement. They were now spinning like the Catherine Wheels. A burning sensation formed in my throat. My heartbeat was steadily rising and becoming more aggressive.

'Hadi, are you listening to me?'

As if my movie was being played in slow motion I turned my head, with a struggle, towards my mother.

36

Had I just heard her speak? Her lips were still moving but only a silent swarm of butterflies flew from her mouth. Raindrops began falling from my mother's eyes. Like a zombie, she stiffly walked over towards me. Before I knew what was happening, she dropped like a dying tulip and shrivelled on top of me.

My mom was sobbing, like a child, whose favourite toy had just been snatched away. Her body heaved, and bumped up and down with each painful cry. I could feel her raindrops of tears. They were damp and warm. Their wetness was causing my T-shirt to stick against my skin. My heartbeat was still chasing itself, not able to keep up. The walls still seemed to be pushing their way in towards us, as if wanting a piece of the gossip. I still hadn't said anything. Not one word. Not one why, or how. Not one question was able to form inside my brain, which seemed more like a tornado, with its whirlwind of thoughts. With the little power I had in my legs, from the weight of my mother's heavy body, I pulled myself up from the pod. My mother's hands gripped the thighs of my jeans, so as not to fall on the floor. My height of six feet must have been more like eight to her. She was on her knees. My head was facing down towards her. My eyes were intensely searing into her waxed, apple red face. 'Where are you going?' she cried.

As I stormed out the house that evening, I didn't even look back. You probably think I'm a cunt. And, how could I leave her crawling on my bedroom floor? I don't really know. But I did. I left the grieving wench on my bedroom floor, while I found the next party.

* * *

It was never my intention to get wasted when I went to parties. It just happened. Like life. I would arrive and people would feed me everything but food. When I look back, I think my status had a lot to do with my popularity. That doesn't help me so much now. I guess there are things that you may want to know about me. Am I handsome? Of course, I am. Am I rich? Of course I am. I am the heir to one of the largest franchises of gas stations this side of the Mason Dixon Line. Elnore Petroleum belongs to us. My mother, the devil curse her, inherited the franchise after my father died. Well, who I believed to be my father, died.

So, there I was, walking down the street I had walked down thousands of times, in my sixteen years of life. Yet this time I felt like a stranger. I paused in the centre of the road and gazed at all the houses that looked the same. The only difference was their colour. They were an assortment of many shades of cream and pink. Who did I actually know? Who really knew me? I wondered how many people in this town knew my secret. I wondered where the people who gave me up could be.

A knife had severed my heart that night. I wished I had a gun. I would swallow its nose and squeeze the silver trigger. I yearned to feel the bullet explode inside me because nothing could be as painful as the pain I felt now. I guess I should feel special because at least someone, who wasn't blood related, loved me enough to care for me. Well, I guess. But you have to know something. Now, this stays between you and me because I hate people knowing my business. But first, I have a party to get to.

Somewhere between my house and East Elm Street the rain had decided to fall. I brushed the fresh drips from my hair and lifted the hood of my sweater over my head. As I passed the Seven to Eleven, I looked through its aquarium sized windows and recognised the bleached blonde hair, poking above one set of shelves. I headed in 'cause I could always do with more cigarettes and gum. The pill was making my jaws move in jagged directions. And water, I could really do with some water. Inside, I found my friends, Ray and Gil. Gil's full name was Gillespie Jake. What the fuck were his parents thinking? People get his name backwards all the time.

*   *   *

As Hadi entered the store, the two boys looked up and greeted him with lazy smiles and puffy, bloodshot eyes. Hadi walked over to the candy shelves where Ray and Gil were obviously having problems. Hadi noticed a handful of chocolate bars in their hands. Their fingers were sifting through the lines of sugar filled treats.

'Hey, Hadi! What's up? Have you heard the news?'

'No. What?'

'Chet, 'the flapper', Carter's lost a bunch of his money. He supposedly had it tied up in shares, or something and it's all gone. Not one iota has he got left. We saw two guys, and it wasn't UPS, knocking at his front door earlier. He's got the blinds down and lights off.'

'Are you serious?'

'Totally.' As Ray was telling his story, he peeled back the wrapper, to his Musketeer and clamped his mouth over half the bar.

38

Hadi had trouble taking his friends seriously because they were somewhere between cloud number five and ten. Ray was referring to Chet Carter, their school principal.

'I'm just on my way to Harmony's. You guys coming?'

'Yeah! Cool.' Ray put the candy he was holding into his coat pockets. He didn't bother looking to see if the sales assistant, by the register, was aware of his antics. Hadi took a quick sweep of the store with his eyes, no one was around. The sales assistant was too engrossed in reading the latest edition of Playboy, and was totally oblivious to them. As they exited the store and headed down the street Ray kept munching on chocolate bars. Every so often he would mutter words under his breath. He was about to speak when Gil said, 'Hadi, have you got your stuff with you?'

'Maybe. But I want something in return this time.'

'What like, money?'

'No.'

'A whore, from the club on Third and Stickler?'

'I want revenge. Oh fucking shit!'

'What?'

'I forgot to get cigs, hold on.'

As I ran back to the store, to revisit my old friend with the Playboy magazine, I drifted like a nomad in my thoughts.

'Oh, I'm so sorry, my love. I didn't mean for it to be this way. I don't know who he was, or who she was. All I know is that your father and I so desperately wanted you… needed you.

'Why? I don't get it.'

'They didn't want you because….' The Catherine Wheels were still swirling around my walls. Like a bird I glided above my mother. I moved my arms up and down, and like a golden eagle I flew away. I escaped her words. Her tongue reached out to touch me with its poison. It had white bumps dotted on its surface; its scaled top layer felt like sandpaper against my face.

'I don't think it was case of not wanting you… I think that some people are just not ready for such responsibilities.'

'That will be five dollars.' The boy had managed to peel his eyes away from the model, who was dressed in a hideously bright, sugar pink bikini. I picked up my cigs, gum and water and headed back to find my clueless friends. Walking down the street, towards the library where I had left Ray and Gil, I wandered past several shops. As I passed the antique store a golden object flashed before my eyes. It was bright and shiny and rectangular, about double of the size of a postage stamp. On the front was an engraving of a lion. There was nothing between me and the object apart from a sheet of glass… only a sheet of glass. I reached through its flowing sheerness and reached for the gold. Bells started to ring. There must be a fire. I couldn't see any fire engines. I placed the gold in the pocket of my hoodie. I had never before noticed the red pockets on my hoodie. The drugs must have really begun taking effect because even my hand was red.

*   *   *

'Dude… where'd ya go, to a fucking tobacco factory? What's that on your hand? Jeez, Hadi, you're bleeding. What did you do?'

Hadi looked down at his hand. 'I dunno, must've grazed it on something.'

'That's more than a graze.'

Gil pulled off his coat and sweater. He had a T-shirt underneath that he removed. He used it to bandage Hadi's hand. The boys headed towards the Oak Hill area of town. Oak Hill was renowned for its ten bedroom mansions that usually housed families of four or less. Hadi had once lived there but when his father died his mother had wanted to stay away from the neighbourhood. She hoped it would help with the loss of her husband.

*   *   *

'You ready, Peter?'

'Not yet, I'm just tucking Hadi in'

'Now, Hadi, you go right to sleep. Your mother and I will be back in the morning. We're going out on the boat for the night. Chris is downstairs if you need her. I don't want you and Harmony talking all night. Did you hear that Harmony?'

'Yes, Mr Hook. I'm nearly asleep already.'

Hadi reached out his tiny hand to touch the side of his father's face and gently pulled him closer. He whispered into his father's ear.

'I know.'

'What do you know?'

'I know. You aren't him, and SHE, She's not mine.'

Hadi's father felt like plugs had been inserted into his nose and mouth. The young boy before him looked vulnerable as he lay covered in his huge duvet. The duvet was wrapped around him several times, even though it was August. He had raised this young boy whose skin felt like satin to touch, and though he was not his own, he had thought that keeping his past sheltered from him would serve as protection.

'We'll talk tomorrow. I love you, son.' The man walked over to the young girl, who was cocooned in a Snoopy sleeping bag on the floor next to Hadi's bed.

'Goodnight, little Princess.' He bent down and kissed her, like a raindrop kisses a rose on a summer's morning. He fondly ruffled her auburn hair.

The man shuffled his feet across the carpet and as he closed the door to block out the hallway light he whispered to his son.

'I'll miss you ... sweet dreams. Dream of Neverland and wish you never have to grow up.'

Hadi shifted onto his side and grabbed the gold locket that hung around his neck, and as though he was pulling on a rope, in a winning game of tug of war, he freed the chain from its lock. He placed the locket in the drawer next to his bed.

Poetry

PENNY BRINNEN

Sunday Sestina

It's not as though I paint this sort of picture
You read it in the papers every day, they note
Refugees, detainees, Eee it's sad as Sundays;
On TV you're not to hear – just read their lips
And t'wireless too! Fibs – the lot's on medication.
Come on Crumpet; let's have Emmerdale and tea.

T-bone steak braised for dinner – what a treat
And shinbone for Crumpet – there's a picture!
Now, where's my rheumatism medication?
Ah; well then, Vera Lynn – now she could hold a note
His Master's Voice playing songs from sweetheart lips,
The day for music, memories and rest – Sundays.

Sundaes from childhood with peaches, nuts and cream
On the pier with stiff breezes and cups of tea
The donkey rides, fish and chips and salty lips
Running on the beach, the promenade, picture
Postcards home; oh Auntie Ethel please take note
We're all well – and don't forget your medication!

Medication is what life's all about these days
Even poor Crumpet's poorly and the vet's closed Sundays,
Then his tummy's seen to, by a vet of note
A quick jab and pills with his Pedigree Chum tea
Will soon have him right, playing ball through the picture
Window, my little bundle – wet nose and wet lips.

Lip stick, best frock and pearls, from Harry – they're real mind;
Continuous love was the best medication.
Fifty year' ago, he'd take me to the pictures
To see Charlie Chaplin and *the talkies*; Sunday's
We'd go walking, then back to his Mother's for tea,
He gave me a ring, golden it was, and a note:

Note said, 'Will you marry me Nelly? My love!'
He traced my face with warm kind hands and touched my lips
With his; we ran to the bandstand and shared squash (tee-
Total). When he died, they prescribed heart medication.
I still see him – near the gardens – each Sunday
On t'hearth, his sepia smile transcends the picture.

Nurse consults her notes and withdraws medication.
Nelly's lips are lily white, pure, like her Sunday
Wake. With brown tea. She's as peaceful as a picture.

The Model Railway Exhibition

An exhibition, of men of a certain age
and hair-loss, bespectacled
are littered about the hall
each – proud fathers
stationed by their babies' sides,
them billowing and their daddies – hooting
tooting, rooting for junior's delayed windies-up
who splutter and hiss as oil is applied:
babies chug and daddies sigh,
glances and pride are exchanged.
Children are hushed – and shushed
'No touching and no leaning – they're not toys you know!'
These men have batteries and will travel.
Mummies are shopping but are destined to call
by, as their journey terminates.
They shunter in – their carriages wide
minding the gap.

Fishing the Severn

A distant rush brings shiny waters
spinning past like sheaths of glass
blindingly bright and shifting with quiet reflection.

A long-legged wader strides from the shore
driving screeching gulls and cormorant, turns
away as he breaks the streaming waves.

Halting mid-flow, motionless
he scans for silver scales, press-ganged
by current – fate or flotsam.

On rooted willow banks
rows of putchers lay silently empty
as unseen salmon slalom the eddies and straits.

Heron-like still, the fisherman
keens the ebb, scents the fret
and there, a fish tacking the bore

and leaping the swell
a caricature of Edward Lear
lave in hand, as if for butterflies,

capers nimbly and nets the salmon
shoulder high, sure-footed,
the sediment subsiding, sliding

he ploughs the transient tide
waist deep. The glacier thawed
will refresh as it withdraws.

SALLY DARBY

Kitchen Window

It is noon.
Air tremors with heat,
Across the street
A tabby cat prowls,
Walks the fence like a tightrope.

Number 2:
A man cleans his car,
While his son strums
A guitar, the notes
Fall through the open window.

Opposite,
A white-haired woman
Leans on her gate;
Clouds recline, benign
On the horizon like smoke.

An oak tree:
Leaves shine like emeralds
In the sunlight.
Sky is brush-swept blue,
Two swallows circle above.

Sunset After Rain

The sky's stage lights up once more
For its main player; all who are present
Applaud its final, valiant display.
The sun gives breath to the rain-soaked day,
Exhaling through disgruntled clouds,
Catching the grass and the trees by surprise;
Touching branches with copper fingertips.
Three single sparrows rejoice in its exit,
Twisting, twirling, the final encore,
A burgundy glow spreads over the hills;
The rolling land brims with lilac hues.
But before the world can revel too long
In the conjured misty golden light,
It has dipped under; until tomorrow.

That Smile

that smile
that lopsided grin   aimed at me
that face   happy
pushes me close to insanity

that smile
i should turn away fast
before i'm hit by the blast
that smile is imprinted on my mind now

that smile
the one that plays on my mind each day
skipping
        frolicking
                making me sway
hypnotised by its silly power

that smile
infectious   it seeps across to me
now i'm the one smiling deliriously
that smile gets reflected in your eyes

that smile
that irresistible expression of joy
cherubically placed on the face of a boy
twisting me   making me wistful

that smile
each time   an indescribable thrill
that smile could kill
today it brought tears to my eyes

AMANDA EVANS

Lust

The sky is clear on the day,
but the rain
has left puddles
on the stadium benches.

The ladies are forced to stand
in their furs.
Throats and arms drip
jewels, like catkins on branches.

They wait for the race to start;
to see those
bodies arching
and falling, lathered in sweat.

The ladies, their skin like bark,
remember
how that sheen felt
slickening trembling thighs.

Vanity

The face of God is set in stone.
An archway soars, mottled
with the rot of passing years
and the weather's probing fingers.

Twin angels flank the entrance.
Stone hands clasp cold breasts,
faces set in granite,
lips press in stony silence.

Beneath, the chapel door.
God's face speaks with a new mouth.
The yellow wood is smooth,
and the glass is shining.

Little Book

The earth was damp when the girl sat down to read
Because it had rained the night before. There
She sat the whole day, using her finger to lead
Her eyes across the pages. She sat in a place where
There used to be tulips in spring, but the weeds
Had invaded, shooting their seeds into the air,

And overpopulating the patch of earth, as weeds
Are wont to do. Still, that patch was where
The solitary girl came to read
From her little, leather-bound book every day, ere
The sun dipped his head in the west to lead
Her home. The next morning would find her there

Again. She came ever alone, though she had led
One other to her spot before, a little boy from Ayr,
A cousin. But he had seen only weeds
In her sanctuary. She was content to remain there
In solitude, listening to the wind that blew through the reeds
On the bank of the small pond near to the patch where

She lived her reclusive life. She had often read,
In her little book, where Adam and Eve had spent their
First days, before Satan's evil had led
Eve to sin. The girl called her private place, where
Grass snakes wove through the long stemmed weeds,
Her Eden, and she fancied herself the heir

To the knowledge that cursed mankind. The weeds
Of paradise grew in abundance in the spot where
She knelt each day to pray, and the brittle reeds
By Eden's lake bowed and snapped in the air,
To lie prostrate upon the ground, following her lead,
Eve and her children communed, their

54

Whispers sent Heavenward. But they plummeted like lead.
Too dense with inherent sin to rise through the air,
The prayers became ensnared by the weeds
That choked her paradise, and the serpents there,
Already tarnished by the tales the girl had read,
Swallowed them. The patch of earth where

The girl sat everyday with her little book to read
Was damp with her tears. Eden's waters led to where
A meadow of flowers had been overrun by weeds.

The girl returned to the garden each day, to sit and talk to the air.

JULIE FRUSHER

Nocturne

Had you been out? Where did you go? Did he see you talking to that man again? Did he see you laughing, blushing, flicking back your hair?

Who turned on the music? Who turned the volume up high?

Legende, from Delibes' Lakme.

It sounds like screaming... high notes, long and drawn out. Makes me think of torture. And then sadness, so much sadness.

And what was the look in his eyes? Did he call you a whore again? Or was he silent throughout

Nocturne No 2.

Precise piano, like a child's music box with a ballerina twirling around aand around in her stiffened plastic pose. Simple and yet somehow menacing. Because she has to keep dancing, she cannot stop. Whenever we open that lid. Again and again she must dance, spin and spin and spin until the rest of the world is a blur. Just a blur.

Was he drunk again? Were you?

Mars, from Holst's Planet Suite.

Sinister. Dark. Heavy. The Bringer of War. The Bringer of violence and pain and the colour red before the eyes. Every note breaks a bone.

And did you feel every blow? Did it hurt? Did you bleed?

Are the bruises darkening, the flesh swelling, breaking open...?

Mahler's Symphony No 1 in D, the Fourth Part.

And now I am being swept away on a tide of something overwhelming. Everything's loud: the music, the colours, his voice. I want to hide. I want to curl into the smallest of balls like a hedgehog hibernating.

Can you feel the rough carpet beneath your skin? See the dirt, the dog hairs, the stray grains of dried rice from yesterday's takeaway?

Barber's Adagio for Strings.

Funeral music. Music to cry to. Music for the end. Lying here, I think I must be dying. It's so peaceful now. Maybe I'll open my eyes and see an angel.

At last … was there silence before a door slammed, a car revved and drove away? Did it hurt to breathe, to move as you reached out your arm towards the phone?

And then, did you pause, just for a little bit, fear in your heart, as you formed the words you should have done years ago … 'police please'.

HARRY HEYWOOD

Meaning

Home,
love.
Safe,
family.
Comfort.
Seek.

Seek
home.
Comfort.
Love,
family.
Safe.

Safe,
seek.
Family,
home.
Love,
comfort

Comfort.
Safe.
Love,
seek.
Home,
family

Family,
comfort
Home,
safe,
seek,
love.

Love,
family,
seek,
comfort.
Safe.
Home.

Seek comfort;
love family;
safe home.

RAY McCRINDLE

Always

I think of   lightning

your eyes   in my eyes:

reflecting   desire

dancing   reels

Water Cycle

Early morning sun plays across your shoulders,
rippling; golden.
By noon your skin is hot.

Pores yield rivulets to the air
forming clouds

that grow heavy; pregnant; waiting.

Shadows glide across your shoulders;
goose pimples rise
to greet the cooling touch.

Clouds open:
Rain is born

falling drop by single drop.

ROWAN MIDDLETON

The Bridge

All night the burning headlights streak the dark,
And by day the well-worn road from the port
Is a crawling column of caravans and cars,
With tired children staring out of windows
At the rusted metal bridge whose girders carry
The wheels that turn for Paris, Berlin and Rome.

Over sixty years ago it was a flag
On a map where arrows pointed from the beaches,
Where bodies washed from the landing the day before,
Where tanks and lorries rumbled off the ships
And Neville Watts marched in a throng of brown and green.

That night he listened to the breath of men in a barn,
Wet feet, runny nose and a head awash with thoughts
Of toast and jam and home where his mother painted
The planes that throbbed above the hissing rain.
The scraps of straw and smell of cow still clung
To their coats as they drank their tea in the empty yard.
They crept away like shades in the morning mist,
To disappear behind a line on the map.

A rush of air made raindrops plop from leaves.
He turned his head, eyes searching the rows of trees,
Then lay back down, concealed in long wet grass.
Beside him George, his beret drooped over an arm,
Was drifting away as his fingers uncurled from his gun.
Neville gently unlooped the binoculars from George's neck.
The empty bridge below stretched dark between
The river banks; men crouched beside the guns.
The church behind was pocked with bullet marks,
A jeep was parked by the splintered glass of the bakery.

Two men were leant against the schoolyard wall
They smoked cigarettes and drank from dented mugs.
That bore the jagged sign of a reverse sun
On the gravel lay silver spanners and the feet of a man
Stuck out from under a lorry, propped on bricks.
When he pulled out his head, his nose was black with grease
They pointed their mugs and laughed – the mechanic shrugged,
He stopped to listen to a humming on the breeze.

Then wumph! The ground beneath Neville turned and shook.
George's head jerked up as a cry pierced their deafened ears
From the village below came the rattle of falling bricks,
The guns by the bridge fired back at the planes in the sky
That faded behind a veil of oily smoke.
Men ran like ants, their laughter cut short like the grass
So carefully trimmed round regiments of clean white stones
Just out of the village, on the other side of the bridge.

La Beauce

The endless fields that roll across the plain,
Are whipped by winds that scour the empty skies,
By towering silos filled with golden grain.

This is La Beauce, whose stark refrain
Of earth and sky recurs, and typifies
The endless fields that roll across the plain,

When wheat is ripe with sun and rain,
From crawling combines dust clouds rise
By towering silos filled with golden grain.

The windmill by the road now stands in vain,
A pin against the clouds, it modifies
The endless fields that roll across the plain.

The yeast and water bring to life again
The dusty flour whose first origin lies
By towering silos filled with golden grain.

Baguettes, croissants, they both contain
The seed grown here, in bread it glorifies,
The endless fields that roll across the plain,
By towering silos filled with golden grain.

The Rain

The rain sweeps the sky,
Smudged with ponderous clouds.
The roofs are shiny
With water that spills down
The broken gutter.
It hits the pavement, splashes,
Courses down the street,
And pours into the dark drains
That run for miles,
Buried below the city.
The water surges
Beneath the traffic lights
And zebra crossings.
Waiting under umbrellas,
We are unaware
Of the torrent that gushes
Underneath our feet;
Until it bursts out of
The concrete culverts
Into the swollen river.
It is swept and carried along
Away to the open sea.

Higgin's Well

Each day we trod the dusty path
To where the water, fresh and cold,
Rushed forth from dark and clammy earth.

We filled our pails all through the year
And brought our cattle in the heat
Their hooves slip-sliding in the mire.

But the daily passage of so many feet
Trampled the ground that Higgin called his own:
The muddied earth would not support his wheat.

One night he rose and set out all alone,
And working fast he sought to dam
And block the spring with rock and stone.

First light showed us the outcome of his plan.
We slowly turned and made our way toward
The far-off valley where the river ran.

As Higgin counted out the grain he'd stored,
He stopped, then heard a splashing sound.
From underneath his floor a torrent poured.

He seized his spade and dug into the ground
At the field's gate, heaving clods and turf.
Until he bent and looked; cried out – he'd found

Beneath his boots the same spring's gurgling mirth.
And free once more, the water fresh and cold
Rushed forth from dark and clammy earth.

The House

We start the footings in the rain,
Shovelling the squelching mud that coats
Our boots, kicking for a foothold
Amidst the clay and broken bricks.
The spades are gritty in our hands
As we dig.

A square of mud lies where the house
Will be. Trudging through the rain
We barrow slopping concrete, hands
Smoothing the liquid floor, our coats
Flapping as we roll out plastic under bricks,
Before the pouring rain.

If it goes on this rain will hold
Us back, he says. The house
Meanwhile has grown, and the bricks
In rows now stand beneath the rain.
We walk about in our damp coats,
Our noses dripping.

From the scaffold he stoops and hands
Me down the bucket that will hold
The grey cement that coats
The ground around the house,
As the mixer in the rain
Churns the 'muck'.

Timbers arch above the bricks
And slates cut sharp into our hands.
The wind has chased away the rain;
Will this fine weather hold?
The sun shines down upon the house
We strip to our shirts.

We trowel and smooth the coats
Of plaster, hiding the bricks
That are the bones of this new house.
The paint is dry beneath our hands:
It all turned out.

The house we built with our own hands
Is not just coats of paint and bricks;
This home will hold.

IAN MORGAN

This Much!

A camel spitting;
Monkeys throwing faeces –
that's how much I love you.

With the brutal rage
of a cuckold husband
or the tender care
of the psychopath.

That's how much I love you.

With criminal conviction
and heartfelt malice;

I love you.

As intimate as torturer's attention
to his favourite subject.

From warm fleshy kisses
to cold ignored caresses.

That's how much I love you.

I just wanted you to know.

Act Naturally

This secret might be bigger than me;
bigger than you.

Such subterfuge:
moments in corners,
kissing behind closed doors.
Captured glances; our eyes
locked.

The price is to smile
when I see her,
to enquire how you are
as if I didn't know
and accept the invitation
to the house you share
together
for wine, food and regulated
truths.

The slow burn of aching
for your touch.
It's perversity: you and her.

You say 'act naturally'.
For me that's to peel down your shorts
and explore you inch by inch
(there's so much left to discover);
to feel the muscles tighten
in your arms;
to taste the sweat off the back
of your neck.

What's natural would be to kiss
you publicly, deeply.

But that isn't what we do;
so I make do with corners,
closed doors and glances;
and make the moments matter.

Winter

My sun hangs low.
Trees shed leaves
like tears;
warmth retreats, allows cold to descend.
A lonely, hardening frost
that blankets.

Once all I saw was you.

I hear no snowstorm, no wind,
no distraction.
My heartbeat prepares for this hibernation,
where I will remain
until your touch
wakes me.

Slice of Lemon

A slice of fresh
lemon dropped
in a glass of gin
retains a certain
dignity.

No ice cubes left
in the tray.
No need anyway.
Sip, sip, then refill
this small glass.

Refresh the slice
with more gin.
The half-done bottle
poured by my callow
hand. Don't look –

manicured nails –
cracked. Don't look –
tired, honey blonde hair,
my wrist clasped in gold;
my dull eyes.

Another drink?
Just one more
to steady the nerves;
to stop the trembling,
the coldness.

Empty. The glass
drained I can
put it down but not
too far away. Cut
the lemon.

CLAIRE OPIE

Gwithian

A rustling hush before the day unfolds. The hiss of traffic like distant waves. We were woken by it; we'd spoken in voices raw with mist and morning. With zips from behind and beside, with torch-light through her fingertips. The floor crackled and creased with sand from sandals. At night, the hot and cold of sanded, salty skin; leaning forward in pub corners. We sat on the beach all day that day. We made things out of sand like oysters and mermaids. She looked closely at the colours; made up stories about where each grain came from; decided that the sea is the best place to lose things. She'd lost a ring in the sea two years before, to join somewhere a crate, a dustbin lid, footballs, bottles, scattered ashes. I listened to her fall asleep, but it wasn't long before those gentle shakes and are you awake are you awake's. No distractions in that murmuring silence. New Years Eve was the worst; after we'd seen the starlings descend onto the marshland. Amazing, wasn't it, wasn't it? Cars stopped to watch the flocks like black ribbon; she made the shapes with her hands. Now, somebody else is listening to her early morning whispering.

MARIANA RUEDA SANTANA

Frustration

The muses abandoned me,
those fucking bitches.
I woke up one day to find my bed empty
and that was that.

I knew they didn't owe me an explanation
so I just waited
to see if they might come back.
But I haven't seen much more since really.

Melpomeme throws pebbles at my window
sometimes when she's drunk.
I've stopped opening
Because she only makes fun of me.
She makes funny faces and
pretends she is me and mock-cries
pointing at my empty pages.

Sometimes Erato joins her, standing there
with a sweet, scorning smile
which is far more cruel than anything else.
And Melpomeme bursts into laughter.
And I curl in bed,
like a baby bean.

They were the ones I loved the best.

Terpsichore still sends me postcards
every once in a while
with a "Calliope says hi" on the side margin.

Clio I left long ago.
She used to hurt me, and Uterpe was always
too cool to hang out with me.
The other ones liked me even less
although they had kissed me mockingly
from time to time.
They came to my bed sometimes when they were bored.
It wasn't pity sex,
it was more like they didn't have anything better to do
than torture me.

I've written Terpsichore back sometimes asking about them.
I told her I wanted to make love to them again, all of them
and she wrote back.
It was a postcard full if giggles
and a tiny note at the bottom:
"We didn't make love
We just fucked"

So I wrote back that I wanted to fuck.
Again.
In every way possible.
I said I
wanted to fuck them like a woman, like a man
like a bird, like a monster, like a river.
That I wanted to lick their penises
And vaginas and breasts and arms.
That I was ready:

To die.

She sent back a postcard with a picture of tiny rolling eyes.

And so I went to my computer
and watched movies.
And ate biscuits.
And slept a little.

And I'm
still alone

with a mine of unwritten verses hidden in my head.

Novella

ADAM PALETHORPE

A Stripper's Story

I could feel my eyes glazing over from the overwhelming
boredom. I was annoyed at myself for even turning up that night, but I
comforted myself in the knowledge that the hounding I would have
received from the lads, had I not come, would probably have been
more boring, and would have lasted a lot longer than this date.

By all accounts I should've felt happy to be on this date. It was the
first one in what had felt like forever, and she was an extremely
attractive girl. That's all I'd really noticed about her when we first met;
she was gorgeous, thin, but exercised, not malnourished, with blonde
hair stretching practically to her bum. Probably the worst thing about
meeting people in bars, though, is that it's so impersonal; you never get
to properly speak to them until you've already expressed your interest
in them, and by then it's a bit late to bail out. I really wish I'd had a
chance to have a real conversation with Victoria.

'So then like James was all like what? And so I was like you twat
James...' she continued in between forkfuls of food.

I couldn't bring myself to listen properly. I'd been secretly
counting the amount of times she'd said 'like', 'y'know' and 'whatever'
in the last fifteen minutes or so. I can't remember how much it was
exactly. I don't care to. I wasn't even sure what she had been talking
about, there was something about her mobile phone and, oh God, she
played her ring tone to me. In a restaurant. I shovelled more of the
greasy battered pork and rice into my mouth and feigned interest a
little while longer, while my mind wandered back to the night I'd
actually met Victoria, a few days ago. I'd also met someone else, you
see.

I'd been in the Hare & Tortoise with Ash and Dave. Their band
was playing an acoustic set, and I'd gone along to listen. They were
pretty good and there was a lively crowd, too. The Hare was the only
place around here that still had any live music, and wasn't entirely
appropriate for it since it was tiny and had a grand total of about
sixteen seats, leaving the other three or four dozen patrons to stand
cramped together. If you listened, you could hear a constant
cacophony of 'excuse me,' 'sorry,' and 'watch it!' as arms were gently

pushed, heels and toes were trodden on and pints were spilled. But the music was good, and the drinks were even better. I first laid eyes on Victoria at the bar, waiting for the round of beers I'd ordered for the band. She'd bounded up next to me with a fiver in her hand and called for a vodka and coke.

'Hey,' she said, 'are you with the band?'

I paid the barmaid and smiled at Victoria. 'No. Well, they're friends of mine and I sometimes help them out with some lyrics, that's about it.' This was a lie, and I wasn't entirely sure why I said it.

'Oh cool so you write songs and stuff?'

'Na,' I smiled, 'I'm not good with music, exactly; I just do the words.'

'I write poetry sometimes, too,' she beamed and sucked at the straw in her drink. It was at this point my interest in this smiling blonde was piqued. I'm a sucker for any pretty girl who can spin pretty words.

'Cool. You'll have to show it to me sometime. I didn't get your name?'

'I'm Victoria,' she replied.

'Adam. Sorry can you excuse me for a moment? The band are waiting for their drinks.' It was a poor excuse to duck out from a blossoming conversation, but I'd already reached that little plateau where I need a short breather to think of something to say that would keep her attention. This was all pretty difficult, I hadn't been 'on the pull' in a couple of years and felt rather self-conscious already. As I turned with the tray, Ash stepped beside me and put his hand on my shoulder.

'Woah, who's that?' he asked as we walked towards the stage.

'Oh, nobody I know – we just got chatting.'

'She's hot. She's checking you out, too. No, don't turn round, you tit.'

'Okay. I'll keep chatting to her; she is really, really good looking. Says she writes poetry, too.'

'Whatever turns you on,' he laughed, 'just know that if you don't get her number tonight there is going to be trouble, okay?'

'Why do you care so much about my love life all of a sudden?'

'Well, you're a mate, and there's a gorgeous girl staring at you. I'd be an arsehole if I didn't care.'

'As opposed to your normal caring arsehole self?' I grinned at him.

'You won't find a more caring, sharing arsehole than mine, Adam.'

'Err, don't ever say that to me again.'

'I gotta start the second half of the set mate. Go and talk to her!'

So I chatted to Victoria for a bit. All the mundane stuff about who we are, where we're from, what we do, all that filler crap that you generally forget by the time you next meet up and end up having to apologise and ask again. And then feel stupid when they've remembered every detail about your obscure occupation. Victoria was really quiet, and didn't seem to ever start a topic of conversation. She was staring at the band whenever I wasn't speaking to her. I couldn't really tell if this was because I was boring her, or maybe she just fancied Ash or whatever. I didn't speak much after a while, either, and just listened to the music. I had heard the songs a dozen times before, of course, but I still enjoyed it. Up until the last song, anyway, when Ash decided to play wingman and throw a wildcard into the mix for me to play with.

'All right. We'd like to thank everyone for coming tonight, we've only got time for one more song and we decided to play a special one to close,' he pointed in my direction, 'our good friend Adam over there wrote the lyrics to this one.'

And he winked at me. The truth is, of course, that I'd had nothing to do with that song, but it's a wonderful slow song with the kind of lyrics that may well have been designed to turn any love-struck individual to jelly.

It did the trick, since Victoria had sidled up to me and was holding my hand less than half way through the song.

*   *   *

Okay, I was being unfair. It wasn't that she wasn't a *nice* girl, just that I couldn't help thinking about the events which transpired after the Hare & Tortoise. I was making excuses to myself in order to avoid becoming attached to Victoria, instead thinking about another girl, Crystal, while Victoria's verbal diarrhoea flowed casually into one ear and out of the other side without apparently touching anything in between.

When the Hare closed up, the band's drummer and bass player packed up their equipment, said their farewells and headed off home. Dave and Ash, however, had other plans. I'd had enough to drink to follow them, since going back to my empty house seemed really unappealing tonight. I clutched the book of matches in my pocket once in a while to make sure it was still there. Victoria had written her phone number on it, and I had every intention of calling her in a day or two. The box itself was a stroke of genius, it actually had a space on the back marked 'Name' and 'Number'.

'I fancy a drink somewhere else,' said Dave, 'where's still open?'

'There's Bar US,' I suggested, 'but that's going to be packed. What time is it?'

'About quarter to twelve.'

'Right, I said, 'that means they'll be playing Bon Jovi right about now. Let's not go there.'

'Good thinking that man,' said Ash, 'but that means the only place left open is that strip club.'

'They serve drinks, we can play cards and there's no glam rock,' Dave laughed, 'so that's fine by me. You up for it Adam?'

'A strip club?'

'Yeah, they refurbished it recently. It's not quite so grotty anymore.'

'But still grotty?'

'Well, yeah. It's a strip club, what did you expect?'

'Okay, whatever. Let's just get some drinks in.'

You can usually tell that a place is a dump when you walk in and the barman is burying his face in his hands with his elbows on the bar, not even noticing that patrons have arrived. The club was empty, but the music was loud enough that it became indistinguishable from someone hoovering a really filthy deep-pile carpet with a decades-old vacuum whilst the old lady next door bangs on the wall with her walking stick in protest of something or other. The vacant tables sat eighteen inches high, surrounded by small wooden crates apparently stuffed with beanbags so that they vaguely qualified as chairs. One table, however, was populated. About eight girls crowded round it, all wearing various glittery underwear, sometimes stockings, but otherwise not much else. Unless you counted inches-deep makeup as clothing, creating faces saturated with shades of red and blue that only the downright pissed could love. There was an eerie, uncomfortable sensation of being stared at; of course there was, since three men had just entered a room inhabited solely with girls dying to make a few extra quid. The barman grunted a good evening and mumbled the price of the round I ordered. I made the fatal mistake of paying with a twenty. This meant that he handed over a tenner as change; the eyes of the girls shifted from us to the money being stuffed back in my wallet.

We took our drinks, thanked the barman, and headed to a table out of sight of the strippers, in the hopes that we could sit down, drink and play cards without being accosted by several pairs of breasts being pushed in our faces. This sounds really odd, but none of us were there for the girls, just to drink in a glam rock-free environment. A strip club is not the ideal place to go for this, since the girls are just trying to get paid and so will do anything to get guys to give them money, even if they don't want a lap dance. I shuffled the cards and dealt three hands. Ash took one look at his, knocked back his drink.

'Pre-emptive,' he said. 'I was going to end up having to drink anyway. Why do you never deal me a good hand?'

I grinned at him, trying to ignore the group of strippers peeking round the corner, whispering to one another. The game was our own personal creation: Pieces of Eight, a bastard hybrid of rummy, poker, a bottle of Captain Morgan's and, whenever it was available, a lot of Chinese food. It's a great game that generally involves a lot of drinking.

I'd barely had time to look at my hand when our table and its unoccupied chairs were suddenly filled with half naked women pretending to pleasure themselves by rubbing their thighs and licking their lips.

'So hey guys, whatcha doing?' asked the girl sat next to me with bleached blonde hair and a stud in her nose. It looked like a little diamond, and I immediately found myself wondering whether it was real or not, and then feeling like a bastard for caring.

'Nothing much,' said Dave, 'just having a late drink and a chat.' I noticed that the guys had thrown their cards in already. I did the same. We were going to get sucked into a conversation that was more or less just a sales pitch, and we didn't have much of a choice about it. I looked at the girls; to my left was the aforementioned bottle-blonde, on my right a really thin brunette with a bad fake tan. On the other side of the table sat Dave and Ash. Ash had a blonde standing behind him with her hands on his shoulders. On Dave's right was a tall black girl wearing white stockings and a minimalistic, but not tacky, matching bra and thong and covered with sequins like the other girls' outfits.

'Quiet tonight then?' Dave continued.

'Oh yes, it's been dead all night,' said the brunette. She sounded South African and her breath smelled of vodka, 'we're so glad you guys turned up. Are you looking for some fun?'

'Not really,' said Dave, 'I'm married.' The girls giggled and Dave rolled his eyes at me.

'How about you, honey?' the pretty blonde asked Ash, who laughed.

'I'm sorry, I've got enough for my cab home tonight and that's about it. I'm just sponging off of him,' he said, pointing at me.

'What makes you think I can afford much else tonight?'

'You're the only one here that isn't a musician, therefore you're probably the wealthiest.'

'Oh, are you guys in a band?' The black girl looked up. It was then that I noticed that she hadn't really been looking at us, really; she was just being scenery.

'Those two are,' I nodded at the other guys, 'I can't even remember how to play the piano anymore, even though I played for years.'

'So what do you do?' she went on.

'Nothing exciting,' I grinned, 'trust me.'

'He's a writer!' Ash jumped in, 'does stories and poems and all that stuff.'

'I'm a terrible poet, Ash, don't lie about that.'

'He's also really modest,' he continued, and Dave started laughing.

'I'm also an arrogant bastard. Don't believe their lies.' I grinned sheepishly. It wasn't funny, but the girls laughed. Generally if you say a sentence, even if it's not funny, but you add a swear word and smile while you say it then you'll get a laugh, or a smile at very least. We'd done this sort of routine before, where we'd lie about one another's occupations, achievements and aspirations, just to see how people react. I've introduced friends at parties with bizarre stories of how they once fought crocodiles, climbed mountains and wrestled with malfunctioning parachutes thousands of feet above the ground. Anything that could actually be possible, but unlikely, works for this purpose. It might not be ethical, but it gets strangers talking to one another whereas they'd probably have hung around with their little clique and never mingled with other guests without a little intervention. My brain wasn't really going full-speed now, since it was well after midnight and I was steadily getting drunk. And, of course, Victoria was invading my thoughts.

This particular strip club employs girls primarily for private dances. There's a stage with a pole, but most of the time the girls just use that when they're bored and trying to attract clients. If you want a dance, you pay and are taken to a curtained-off booth to be entertained. After we'd finished our drinks and bought another round, the girls started to get the hint that we weren't really interested in a dance that night. The two blondes wandered off back to the group on the other side of the club, to be interrupted as two new guys walked in and almost immediately wolf-whistled them. They'd linked arms and taken them to a table in seconds. I could see the two still sat with our minor party were eager to actually earn some money, since their eyes turned to their colleagues with an air of annoyance and envy.

'So boys,' said the South African girl, 'do you want a dance tonight?'

'Not really-' I began,

'You wanna see my pussy?' she continued. At this point I felt my eyes rolling. At the same time I felt a little bad that she was reduced to that sort of crap for money, though I quickly reminded myself that there were plenty of guys that would've coughed up a twenty the instant they heard that particular word, so there was no problem.

'Look,' I said at last, 'my friends don't have enough cash left on them, they've already told you that,' but then I felt a sudden urge within me, a ridiculous urge to amuse myself if only for a while, 'but I've got plenty left tonight. Amuse me.'

Almost simultaneously, the South African and the black girl reached for my arms and each grabbed an elbow. Ash and Dave gave a distinctive snigger and then turned to converse with one another, with only brief flickers of their pupils acknowledging that I existed.

'Wait, wait,' I continued, 'I don't particularly want a lap dance. I've got a better idea.'

'What's that?' asked the black girl.

'I haven't written a story in ages, total lack of inspiration. Tell me an interesting story about something that's happened in your life.'

'That's… weird,' said the brunette,

'Yeah, I know. But I'm willing to pay the price of a private dance and all you have to do is hold my attention for ten minutes. You don't even have to take your clothes off.'

'You really just want to talk?'

'No, I want to listen while you talk. Easy money for you, a story for me. And it's really dead here tonight, so you're probably not going to be missing out on some big spender.' I grinned.

'All right,' said the brunette, 'but I can't think of anything. How about you?'

'Does it have to be true?' asked the black girl.

'How would I know if it wasn't true? As long as it's believable, it's good.'

'I'll do it then,' and she led me off to the private booths. The South African girl motioned to walk back to Dave and Ash, but instead wandered back to the strippers' table where a dozen eyes were focused on me and my temporary partner as she pulled the curtains to.

*   *   *

Many armchair psychologists have talked about the existence of the 'chivalry factor', a bizarre little character trait that pops up in almost all men. Since we're socialised to believe that girls are pretty and nice and grow up playing with dollies and plastic saucepans and then bloom into delicate flowers that need protecting from the dangers of the outside world and the evil that men do. There might have been a little cynical hyperbole there, but you get the idea. The funny thing is, this theory is actually not complete bollocks, eager as we may be to dismiss it as such. I will admit that, despite my best efforts, part of me always feels the need to be the courageous prince charming whenever a maiden doth despair. Most of the time I manage to remind myself that my own arse is generally more important (from my point of view, at least) but I, like most men, have found myself getting into trouble because of women. It makes a good story, at least.

Lady Ice, the attractive black girl in the skimpy pearl-white outfit, revealed to me that her real name was Crystal. I felt strangely honoured. We chatted about nothing in particular for a few minutes – more 'getting-to-know-you' crap, and pretty soon I'd forgotten that I was even paying for this conversation. Then Crystal told her story.

She'd grown up near Leeds, with her mother and older sister (the father having left when Crystal was still in the womb, and never contacted since). She told me about her life at home and it actually sounded very happy and content. Her big sister looked out for her a lot. They were a poor family, and as a result the sisters took plenty of abuse from bullies at school, a large helping, you could say, with a side order of racism. She quickly learned not to put up with it, but this only meant she was regularly in fistfights in and out of school with anyone who let slip any snide comments directed at her. In her early teens, big sis had married and moved away, and the happy family disintegrated somewhat. Her mother had started hitting the bottle in a big way; sometimes forgoing food for the sake of a bottle of vodka so cheap you couldn't distinguish it from turpentine. Teenage Crystal, raised to be strong and able to stand alone in the face of adversity, sought means to provide for the household. Being young, black and not particularly well educated left her with practically zero options.

Then she met Miguel. A friend of a friend introduced them at a house party. Miguel was twenty and peddling low-grade chemicals to kids too young and dumb to know the difference anyway. The prick was doing pretty well for himself in his niche balance of being low-profile enough to go unnoticed but able to mark up enough to make it relatively lucrative. Crystal, with holes in her trainers, rejected his sales-pitch since she couldn't afford it anyway. That's when Miguel offered her a job.

He said he wanted to branch out just a little more, but needed someone to help him out. So Crystal could buy crap from him at a small discount then sell it on to make a little bit of money for herself. Exactly why he trusted Crystal not to just turn him in, or rat him out if she got in trouble, I have no idea, but then the guy didn't strike me as being particularly bright anyway. Of course, this was the beginning of the end for her life in Leeds.

*　　　*　　　*

'Hey, I had a lot of fun tonight,' said Victoria, putting her hand on the taxi door, 'thank you for dinner.'

'No problem,' I replied, 'it was good to see you again.' 'Good': it's such a crappy adjective yet I seem to use it frequently in conversation. It ranks up alongside 'nice' and 'cool'. I noticed that Victoria had removed her hand from the door and was seductively close to me.

'Call me?' she breathed into my ear, putting her hands on my shoulders.

'Sure,' I whispered. And then she kissed me. It was a good kiss; that is, it was highly enjoyable and I could not really fault it but my brain was still not paying attention enough to think of any adjective less atrociously dull than 'good'. A little while later I was on my way home. I'd decided to walk, the night was warm, the stars were all out and the streets were quiet. It's only about half an hour's walk back to my house from town; I was used to the walk and on nights like this I generally enjoyed it. It's a time to think, reflect and meditate on whatever situations the day had thrown at me and, perhaps more importantly, an opportunity to sing quietly under my breath as I stride down the dim paths towards the comfort of my bedroom, some music and a whiskey nightcap.

I was humming to myself when something hit the back of my head.

*   *   *

It hurt a lot. It really, really fucking hurt. My ribcage felt like it couldn't take many more kicks so I rolled over in the hopes that the other side was still able to withstand some damage. I had no idea who the hell these guys were, but they hadn't even tried to steal anything from me, they just seemed intent on beating the hell out of me. I thought maybe they wanted to kill me, but then I thought that if they wanted to kill me they wouldn't just be kicking me. They could easily have stabbed me and got a much cleaner job done. There was blood pouring from my nose and, I guessed, my forehead since there was a warm moisture oozing into my eyes. I could just make out the glow of a streetlight from my right eye; there was nothing but pain and darkness in the left. They were yelling something as they beat me; I couldn't make any of it out, not dying was my only priority, what they were screeching could wait as far as I was concerned.

The blows stopped and my attackers talked amongst themselves. I rolled on to my stomach and coughed. Blood spattered on the pavement and I laid my head beside the resulting art project. 'This pussy ain't gonna be a problem, Miguel,' one of them said to a black guy in the driver's seat.

*   *   *

Crystal had worked for this small-time dealer for a while, mostly just peddling pot and, after gaining some trust from her lowlife employer, a few of the more expensive products.

Eventually, a more lucrative opportunity arose for these part-time drug peddlers. Miguel had somehow managed to get some sort of deal on a pretty sizeable coke shipment from the Continent. I don't know many of the details on who exactly was bringing the drugs over or how they'd planned to smuggle them through airport security, and to be frank I don't particularly want to know. But Miguel had offered Crystal a heck of a lot of money to be the one that collected the shit from the airport. He claimed she'd get half of the profits, though Crystal admitted she was completely stupid to believe him. But she'd agreed, and turned up to complete the deal; she was to take the drugs, deliver the money and get her butt back to Miguel as quickly as possible.

The whole thing could possibly have been done flawlessly. Fate decided to throw a spanner in the works, or at least it threw a young homeless kid in. Crystal was stood around waiting for whoever it was that was meant to be delivering the goods. The plane had been delayed by just over an hour. All of a sudden, a young teen charged forward and grabbed her bag, which was stuffed full of cash. She chased him through the busy lounge, causing quite a commotion, when a helpful bystander grabbed the runaway kid and made him trip. This sent the stacks of money flying amidst the bustling crowds and, of course, attracted the attention of the security guards within a few minutes.

Anyway, I was bleeding and needed help. There wasn't really time to be thinking about a stripper's story; I needed a hospital. My attackers hadn't taken anything; they'd sped off in a car just as suddenly as they arrived, so I still had my mobile phone. I called myself an ambulance and pressed my cheek against the coarse concrete. The blue light from my phone was actually incredibly comforting, it glowed and illuminated the little bumps of the pavement, casting a million tiny shadows. It's amazing how much detail you can take in sometimes. When you're in this sort of pain your first instinct will be how you should go about relieving it, the second will be how you should take your mind off of it. It's like your brain kicks into some crazy function that decides that shadows from the floor's texture are more interesting than you ever imagined possible and so it focuses every resource you have on staying alive and finding new aspects of a particular texture to examine in great depth.

*　　　*　　　*

My phone bleeped to indicate I had received a text message. It was still in my hand, so I flipped it open and read the message:

'Hi! Am home now. Just txting to say thx again for 2nite i had a lot of fun. Call me k? sweet dreams hon xxx'

Well, at least Victoria had a pleasant evening. I looked at the ant that was scuttling about busily near my hand and, for a moment, felt really sorry for all the ants that I have in any way injured, intentionally or not, and I then passed out and didn't have a single sweet dream.

*　　　*　　　*

A couple of days passed. I spent most of them in a total haze, nursing my eye – which had swollen to golf ball proportions and gingerly rubbing arnica on to a fractured cheek. My lip had been quite nastily split and the wound had gone some distance into my mouth, requiring stitches.

'Did you know that you have almost as many nerves in your lips as in your fingertips?' the doctor had said, carefully measuring some anaesthetic in a terrifyingly long-needled syringe, 'that's probably why kissing is so much fun.'

'Yeah?' I mumbled, drowsy and nauseous from those foul things you have to drink before an x-ray. I'd waited three hours in a hard plastic chair for the x-ray and hadn't been allowed to take any painkillers in that whole time. I'd been drifting off to sleep but a nurse would periodically poke me and remind me that I was probably suffering from a concussion and should stay upright. An old man who smelled terrible had come in after the first hour and within twenty minutes was complaining about the wait. There were two children screaming hitting each other with plastic hammers while the mother sat reading an old issue of *Hello* magazine and somehow not noticing that the youngest of the two started crying at the top of her lungs, leaving me to plug my ears with my fingers, close my eyes and then get poked by the wandering nurse for the third time. I wondered if she was actually paid to just poke people, then thought of the advert she must've applied to in a newspaper: *'Full time employee required to poke sleepy patients, good starting pay and benefits'.* This made me to chuckle to myself, but that just resulted in a nice spatter of blood trying to escape my lips as the laugh turned into a cough.

'Yep,' the doctor continued, 'so just to let you know… this is going to hurt. A lot.'

'I don't think I can feel anything except pain anyway, I'm not sure that I'll notice.'

I could swear I saw the bastard grin just before I closed my eyes, not wanting to watch the needle stick into my lip. And, oh God, did it ever hurt. My knuckles all clicked in unison as I clamped my fingers around the arms of the chair; when I opened my eyes my hands were noticeably white.

But two days later and I was sore, and my head was thumping, but I was okay. I'd called up my good friend Andy to tell him what happened, I didn't really know why, just felt like telling everybody that I was alive. I hadn't spoken to anyone at all since the attack, and Andy always seems like a logical choice; he's been with me through various troubles and adventures since we were kids.

'Hey man, I brought you something to make you feel better!' he grinned as I opened the front door. Bless him; he'd picked up a bottle of Bushmills, my favourite Irish whiskey, on his way over. I laughed.

'I can't drink; I'm taking about fifteen tablets a day all of which say 'do not drink whilst taking this medication, ever. No seriously, we really, really mean it.' But I'm sure it'll come in handy at some point in the near future.'

'Mind if I open it anyway?'

'Go right ahead, grab yourself a glass from the kitchen.'

I closed the door behind him, then slumped pitifully on the sofa and put my feet up. Andy popped open the bottle in the kitchen, poured himself a measure and walked back and sat in the armchair opposite me, like a psychiatrist with a drinking problem.

'So what have you done this time?' he smiled at me and had a sip.

'Err, I'm not entirely sure.'

'You haven't been messing around with married women again, have you?'

'No! At least I don't think so. I went on a date the other day then on the way home these guys got out of a car and beat the hell out of me. I've no idea who they were.'

'Did they rob you?'

'Didn't take a thing. Just decked me and left.'

'Okay, so it's safe to assume you've pissed someone off?'

'Maybe. Maybe they were just dicks that felt like putting someone in hospital.'

'Well, you get shitty kids doing that, yeah, but a bunch of grown men driving up to you in their car and doing it?'

'I have no idea, mate.'

'You didn't tell me you had a date, by the way. Who was she?'

'Oh, this girl I met at Ash and Dave's gig.'

'Is she nice?'

'She's really good looking.'

'Did the date go well?'

'She thought so,' I smiled, 'but I can't say the conversation did much for me.'

'Your standards are too high, dude.'

'You say that, but you won't believe what else happened.'

'What?'

'I ended up becoming friends with a stripper from that crappy club in town.'

'Err, what?'

I told him the story. I hadn't actually spared a thought towards Crystal's story since the attack. It wasn't something that particularly sprang to mind, for two days I'd just been watching the clock and waiting for four hours to pass so I could take some more medication; I felt like that guy in *Misery*.

I felt a little bit grateful that I didn't have Kathy Bates menacing my every waking moment, though.

*   *   *

The police came along to question Crystal fairly quickly. If the wads of cash flying from her bag hadn't been suspicious enough, the little baggie with a bunch of less-than-kosher looking powder that one of the guards had found underneath a tenner certainly was. It had been pretty downhill from there. The airport security detained her immediately until the police arrived. She knew she was in trouble, and cursed herself for being stupid enough to leave drugs in her bag along with the cash. It's possible she could've gotten away with having stacks of cash on her, she could maybe have claimed she was buying a ticket to go visit a sick relative or whatever and hadn't been to the bureau de change just yet. But the drugs landed her in the proverbial shitter.

The police badgered her long enough for her to miss the deadline with the smugglers, but she squealed on them anyway, in the hope of getting some sort of leniency. They were nowhere to be found. But she still had a chance by implicating Miguel in the whole mess, and get a reduced sentence. She did her best to avoid this, but eventually gave in. Both of them were later convicted, Miguel's home was raided and his stash seized. Crystal was fortunate enough to not have anything except the stuff in her bag. She eventually confessed to me that it had been coke for her own personal use, having tried it on a whim and developed quite a taste for it.

And that was that; she did a few months in prison for possession, a few more of community service and then found herself completely unable to find employment. She headed south to stay with a friend and hoping to find work, but eventually ended up at the strip club as a very final resort.

'I don't mind the work, exactly. It's quite fun when you're actually dancing for someone,' she told me, 'but the pay is awful and the management are not nice men at all. Plus all the girls here are coked up, they're my friends I guess but I don't feel right here. You know you can go out back and buy coke basically any time you want? I hate that part of it. I've tried so hard to be clean so I can start again and being here makes me feel like I'm still in the same position I was when I was in four years ago.'

'You know,' I said, 'you have no idea who I am, and you've just told me something that could get you and all your colleagues in deep trouble. For all you know, I'm an off-duty police officer.'

Her eyes widened and she looked terrified. In the split second before I spoke again I could swear there were tears welling in her eyes, but she was strong; she wasn't going to let a stranger see her vulnerable.

'Don't worry, I'm not.'

She relieved, exhaled and leaned her head back on to the wall.

'What I mean is,' I continued, 'you sound like you really wanted to tell someone how unhappy you are. You've bottled it up so much that when you got an opportunity for release it was like a bottle of champagne from a limo that's been driving off-road for a few hours, shaken up a bit more and then opened.'

'What?' she laughed, 'What the hell does that mean?'

'I'm sorry, I've been having trouble with my similes lately. I thought about seeing a doctor about it but was worried about getting my metaphor laughed at.'

She was laughing so hard that there were actually tears now.

'What I meant was that you just blurted out everything to a complete stranger. But I have to ask you something.'

'What's that?'

'Before you led me here, you asked if your story had to be true or not.'

'You want to know if it was true?'

'Yeah.' I replied.

'Yes, it was.'

'Promise?'

'I promise.'

She leaned over and kissed me on the cheek.

'Thank you for listening. You know I think a lot of the girls here could do with someone who's willing to sit here and just listen to their crap.'

'Honey, if I had fifteen quid to hear every one of their stories I'd probably pay it. I don't, though.'

'Don't poets earn much then?'

'I'm not a poet,' I laughed, 'I write stories once in a while but that's about it.'

'Are you going to write a story about me then? Are you just here for inspiration?'

'That wasn't my intention, but I will probably end up writing something.'

'If you do, will you come back here and give me a copy?'

'No.' I said, ''cos you won't be here in this dump, you'll be doing much better for yourself somewhere.'

*　　*　　*

Andy was in fits of laughter.

'You really paid a stripper just to sit and talk to you for an hour?'

'Yeah. It sounds dumb but it was actually worth the money. She ended up feeling better, I got to hear a story and I got drunk and staggered home singing to myself, great night out if you ask me.'

'Still don't see any reason why those guys jumped you.'

'Probably just random thugs, mate. I'm pissed that I didn't get the registration number or anything. Not that the police would've done anything much anyway.'

'They'd 'make enquiries', probably.'

'Exactly.'

I was in a much better mood now, feeling a lot less sorry for myself. The two of us caught up with each other for a while, which was great. I seem to see Andy less and less over the last couple of years since our various drunken adventures had subsided and work and money started to seem more important than they had done. I think that's part of getting older. I made a promise to myself to contact my old friends a little bit more frequently and hopefully I wouldn't have to get hospitalised just to have something to talk about. I took some more tablets, rubbed more cream into my face and we headed to the local pub to play pool for a while. This was a Sunday afternoon tradition that I had missed.

Later that night, after Andy had headed home, I called Victoria. I'd remembered that she'd sent me a text message right when I was busy getting my face rearranged by the world's worst makeover artists; I hadn't responded and felt oddly guilty.

'Hey! How have you been?'

'Not too bad,' I lied, 'sorry I didn't call you sooner, I've been pretty preoccupied the past couple of days.'

'Oh, that's okay, me too. It's been a mad few days actually, my brother's having a mate of his to stay so I called a couple of mine and we've had a sort of party weekend. He's off again on Tuesday so we're going out to a club or something tomorrow night; I was going to text you to invite you. You wanna come?'

'I'd love to, but I'm so exhausted; I think I'm going to have a quiet week this week. Sorry.'

'Aw, come on, I'd love to see you again. You can come round mine after if you like.'

All right, I thought, that means she wants to sleep with me. And she is cute, if a little dumb. Maybe I'll go… oh God but I look like a wreck with my face all swollen like this and stitches in my lip. And so the train of thought continued until I remembered I was supposed to respond.

'Err, tell you what: I'll get an early one tonight and see how I feel in the morning, yeah? I'll let you know by lunchtime tomorrow.'

'Okay honey, I'll see you tomorrow night,'
'Hopefully!'
'Definitely!' she giggled. I faked a chuckle.
'Okay, goodnight.'
'Night!'

After a brief wrestle with the wretched child-proof cap, I swallowed two more painkillers with the help of a measure of whiskey. I was asleep the moment my fractured cheek touched the pillow.

*   *   *

The next morning heralded a lift in the fogginess internally, a reduction of the external swelling and, better still, my favourite sound: rain pattering against the windows. I'd made the decision to take a few days off work at some point when I was still in the hospital, probably when the kids were doing their best banshee impressions, though whose death the screeches were foretelling I wasn't too sure. I rolled out of bed slowly, expecting my brain to slide to one side like a heavy bag of brazil nuts. It seemed to stay in one place for now, which was a small blessing; I didn't feel quite so terrible. I called work and left a message on the answering machine. I intentionally called early so I could simply say very roughly what happened and not have to put up with a million questions about the details. They could speculate freely. With any luck I'd turn up in a few days time and the rumour mill would have created gems like 'hey did you hear what happened to Adam? Yeah he got in a fight with a gang of hairy lumberjacks, broke every bone in his body. Last I heard he was on a life support machine over in Oxford' or similar.

I stood watching the rain pummelling the frosted glass in the bathroom while I brushed my teeth, flinching as the bristles brushed past the stitches inside my mouth, then washed and shaved, scraping hard sleep from my eyes with one finger as I dreamily got rid of three days' stubble.

A little while later, Andy rang to see how I was getting on. I was actually feeling pretty good, relatively speaking, and my eye, though bruised, returned to fairly normal proportions.

'Still blurry about the whole thing,' I told him, 'I feel like I'm missing something. But that's just probably me trying to uncover a conspiracy that doesn't exist.'

'Probably. Good that you're feeling better though.'

'Yeah. Oh yeah! I have a date tonight!' I laughed.

'Not with the stripper?'

'No, no. I'm supposed to be seeing Victoria again.'

'I thought you didn't fancy her?'

'I thought she seemed boring. But after some thinking she seemed okay the first time I met her, so maybe she was just nervous?'

'Maybe. You going to turn up with your face all messed up?'

'It's not quite so bad today. Besides, scars look manly, right?'

'No.'

'Oh well. But yeah, maybe things will be different tonight, she wants to go to a club. Less awkward than dinner.'

'Cool. Okay good luck then mate, have a good night.'

'And you, see you later.'

*   *   *

Victoria sent me a text message to let me know that she'd be in Bar US from about nine, and that she hoped to see me there and if the amount of 'x's at the end of the message was anything to go by, she was feeling affectionate. After an entire afternoon of trying basically any ointment I could find in the bathroom cabinet to ease the bruising a little, and having very little success, I drove into town.

True to form, the club was already filled to the brim with cheese; 'Sweet Child O' Mine' was just finishing up with Axl Rose's trademark half-bagpipe half-injured-persian-cat noise and led straight into Robbie Williams' breakthrough smash 'Let Me Entertain You'. Wonderful stuff. I spotted Victoria at the bar swaying her hips and drinking cherry VK through a neon yellow straw. And she did look hot, I'd have to admit that.

'Hey, you,' I said, putting my hand around her waist.

'Hey!' she turned round and went to kiss me and then noticed the damage, 'oh God what happened? Are you all right?'

'I'm fine. Got into a bit of a fight the other night is all.'

'After you saw me?'

'Yeah.'

'Why didn't you tell me?'

'Oh I didn't want to worry you. It was just a couple of idiot teenagers that went for my wallet. I floored one of them before another two of their mates turned up and smacked me about a bit before running for it.'

'Aw you poor baby,' she kissed me gently, 'that's so horrible.'

'It's nothing, really, just a split lip and a black eye. I'm fine.'

'I will do my best to make you feel better. Oh hey, Adam this is my brother Ian. Ian, this is Adam that I was telling you about.'

'Oh, hi there, Adam.' The sharply-dressed guy shook my hand; Victoria disappeared to the bathroom. 'Oh, you're Icy's friend, right?'

'What?'

'You know Crystal? From the club?' his voice was oddly stern.

'Oh. Well, sort of, yeah. How do you know her?'

'I'm the manager there. I saw you last week,'

Well, that instantly predisposed me to dislike this guy, since I know all about his little dealings on the side.

'Oh right, yeah. I don't really know Crystal, just chatted to her for a bit.'

'It's okay, I won't tell my sister,' he laughed humourlessly, 'you want a drink?'

'No, no, I'm good thanks. Taking a few painkillers, not really meant to drink.'

'All right, let me know if you change your mind. Sorry mate please excuse me, I just gotta go speak to someone.'

'No problem,' I said. Something made me immediately suspicious about Ian, not just his drug trafficking but also something about his manner. When his back was turned I slunk away from the bar and towards the foot of the stairs which led to the upstairs pool tables and toilets. From there I kept an eye on him, trying to see whom it was he'd strode off to see. They were on the far side of the circular bar in the middle of the room and the staff, pacing busily back and forth getting drinks for a hundred thirsty punters, kept obstructing my view. Eventually I ran up the stairs and hoped for a slightly better view from the observation windows in the poolroom. I was feeling paranoid and wasn't entirely sure why just yet.

And then I saw to whom he was talking, and his face surfaced a very recent and unpleasant memory.

*   *   *

The metal steps clattered and shook violently as I fled down the fire escape. In a moment of panic I'd decided to avoid the club's only normal exit, since it would have put me in clear view of someone whom I did not particularly want to recognise me, and instead opted for the emergency exit. The steps were wet and slippery from the day's rain and for brief moments it felt more like I was surfing down a jagged wave rather than running.

A few minutes later I was stuffing a five-pound entrance fee into the hand of the strip club's bouncer and making my way inside as quickly as I could. Crystal was stood at the bar, working her charm on a potential client. Panicked and shaken I strode to her side and laid a hand on her shoulder.

'Well hello- oh! It's you! Oh god what happened to your eye?'

'Tell me something… this Miguel you mentioned. Tall guy? Dark skinned? Jagged scar on his forehead like some sort of wannabe-gangster-Harry-Potter cross?'

Crystal looked incredibly frightened, which told me all I needed to know.

'That's him, isn't it?' I continued.

'How do you know him?'

'I don't,' I replied, 'but I think I just saw him, and I think you're in trouble.'

'He's here?'

'No, he's over at Bar US at the moment but since I just legged it I'm pretty sure he's going to do his best to find me and, subsequently, you. He's what happened to my eye- he beat the Christ out of me – well, at least some goons of his did.'

'Shit shit shit.' She turned to the guy she'd been talking to. 'I'm sorry, I have to run.'

In just one instant in Bar US, I'd identified my attacker and suddenly remembered what I'd heard the thugs saying after they'd beaten me up and left me bleeding: Miguel. I cursed myself for it not lighting up a bulb in my brain, not even one of those fruity energy efficient ones that take little enough power to light that you could buy hamsters on treadmills and *still* save money. I blamed the concussion but was still angry. Finding Crystal had, for whatever reason, leapt to the top of my list of priorities right after the usual 'Don't Die', but I don't think that counts since that's the usual number one goal for anyone of sound mind.

Holding my hand tight, she dragged me into the back room. Sure enough, there was some emaciated waif of a girl doing a line before she started work. She was practically naked, but looked more like a ribcage with breasts, and thin hair exhausted from bleaching, than an actual woman. My stomach seemed to physically turn. Crystal let go of me to grab her few belongings then ushered me out of the fire exit at the back. We ran down a couple of alleys then back on to the main street, a couple of hundred yards away from the two clubs, and then walked down to the public library. It was well lit with CCTV all around the little area of seating by the defunct water fountain between the kid's playground and the library itself. The two of us collapsed on a bench to catch our breath.

'Any suggestions on what to do? We can't keep running away. I mean, I probably could because Miguel doesn't have a clue who I actually am, but he knows where you work and he's friends with your boss, apparently.'

'What, Ian?'

'Yeah.'

'How do you know that?'

'Well they were just chatting away in Bar US.'

Crystal rubbed her eyes with her fingertips and sat slumped forward with her elbows on her knees.

'Are you all right?' I asked,

'What the fuck do you think?' she snapped.

'Okay, stupid question.' I was rather taken aback by that, but I guess I should've expected it.

'It's because of me that Miguel got sent down, and now he's tracked me down and it's probably not so he can pay for a lap dance, you know? I haven't seen him since I left the courtroom and I don't want to start now. And why the fuck are you involved in this anyway?'

'I have no idea. I hadn't really thought about it. But please stop yelling at me.'

'Okay, okay, I'm sorry. But why would Miguel come after you?'

'Well, maybe if Ian is a buddy of his then he thinks I'm your boyfriend or something? I mean, we were in that booth for a really long time.'

'That's stupid.'

'Thanks.'

'What?'

'Me being your boyfriend, that's stupid.'

'Oh,' she actually stifled a laugh, or at least it sounded like a laugh, 'that's not what I meant.'

'I know.'

She still hadn't uncovered her face. I suspected she was crying, but doing a really good job of hiding it. The *Blade Runner* theme tune started up in my pocket, oh, the wonderful world of novelty ringtones: inappropriate regardless of the situation. 'Victoria calling' the blue screen announced. Wonderful. I decided to answer it. For all her very, very minor faults, Victoria didn't seem like the sort that would be involved in Ian and Miguel's business affairs, and with any luck she might even be able to help me out.

'Hey,' I answered it. There was a tinny sound coming through the speaker that sounded a lot like 'You Give Love A Bad Name'.

'Hiya, where did you go? I've been looking all over for you. Ian and his friend ditched me so I'm all alone here.'

'You're alone?'

'Yeah I'm standing outside US right now.'

'Okay cool. Wait there, I'll be there in a moment.'

'Okay!'

'I'll be right back,' I told Crystal, stuffing my phone away, 'if you see anyone, hide.'

'Hide where?'

'Anywhere. Preferably somewhere with a camera nearby.'

'Don't go without me.'

'I'll be right back. You're safer up here than near that shitty club.'

And I jogged off back to meet Victoria. Maybe she'd be interested in what her brother had been up to.

*   *   *

It was really difficult explaining to Victoria exactly what was going on. I wasn't sure why I was even telling her anything about it, but I supposed it was better that she found out this way rather than a while later when her flat door gets kicked in and the police discover the coke stash in her brother's room, but that might never happen and she could live peacefully ignorant of the situation for the rest of her life.

But I guess, well, I did still kinda fancy her and was hoping for a date where she wasn't incredibly nervous. Yep, I'd filed all her previous shortcomings under 'nerves', maybe I'm a gullible fool but never mind, she was attractive enough to warrant finding out.

I told her what had been going on as I walked her back to the library, constantly looking round for Miguel and Ian. In short, I had to tell her 'hey, your brother is a drug-dealing low life who happily hands his dancers over to gangs of other drug-dealing low lives and also gets random civilians put in hospital just in case they happen to be the aforementioned dancer's boyfriend.' In a nice way, too. It wasn't easy. To my surprise, she took it pretty well. Her first question was:

'So you're seeing someone else?'

'What?'

'The stripper.'

'No! That's the point.'

'Why did you go to Ian's club anyway?'

'Well, it was just for drinks at first, I only went there because Bar US sucks. Then I got chatting to this girl, just chatting, that's all. I felt sorry for her. And before you ask: no, nothing has ever happened between us.'

'I wouldn't mind, you know. That was before we went on a date anyway.'

'Good, but I promise you there's nothing going on.'

'So why are you telling me this? I don't really want to hear about whatever horrible crap Ian's landed himself in, that's his business.'

'I thought you should know, that's all. Plus I wanted to make sure I at least had you on my side.'

'What makes you think I'm on your side?' she stopped walking and I turned to face her. My heart seemed to stop and then, a moment later, beat in triple time to catch up, had she set me up? I was about to say 'what', but suddenly thought that a little eloquence might go an extremely long way. I didn't really have any other option.

'Because you seem like a really sweet, genuine person. I don't think you want to see me get in trouble, and I think you have enough kindness in your heart to have some concern for this poor girl who is in very real danger from your brother's friends,' I paused to breathe, 'plus, I think you're gorgeous and want to take you out again sometime.'

She looked coldly at me, and I was waiting for something to hit me. I was pretty sure I sensed something lurking in the alley a few feet behind me, but didn't want to turn to look. Time seemed to stand still as I watched her eyes. Then her open eyelids flickered and a smile broke out on her face, and she started laughing. She clasped her hands on my cheeks, which made me wince, and planted her lips firmly on mine. It took a moment for my mind to switch out of paranoid-mode and back to what was actually happening, but as soon as it did I had my arms around her waist and reciprocated. It was a kiss full of relief and general horniness.

'Come on, let's find your friend,' she said.

*　　*　　*

Crystal wasn't on the bench where I'd left her. I swore and went to look around. I didn't want to shout just in case the thugs had shown up and... no. Mustn't resort to my old friend pessimism again. But Crystal's disappearance was certainly unnerving.

The play area was very poorly lit, it was just a mass of eerie shadows cast by second-hand light that the library had finished using and cast aside. That would be a perfect place to hide, should she have run into trouble. But it was also, obviously, a great place for trouble to hide too. Still, I felt a lot safer with Victoria at my side. I doubted very much that Ian would get involved in anything much with his sister there watching. Or would he? He didn't exactly seem like the strongest moral character in the world. It felt a little ridiculous to be clutching her hand as I led her down the stone steps towards the playground.

Our breath was coming out as white clouds, the temperature seemed to have dropped an awful lot in the last half an hour. The dark playground seemed to sprawl and one of those little rocking-horse-on-a-spring things was casting a horrifyingly long, menacing shadow over to the climbing frames, slides and an oversized, multi-seated see-saw.

'Crystal?' I hissed. There was no reply.

Then there was a reply, a muffled scream of surprise, very much like a noise of shock from someone creeping up on you and clasping a hand over your mouth. That's probably what it was.

'Over there!' Victoria whispered and raced off towards the little patch of trees a few yards away from the playground.

'Wait! Wait!' I called after her, and she stopped. 'Let me go in first. Don't get involved unless you really have to.'

'But they'll hurt you,' she said, 'Ian won't touch me.'

'Ian won't, but Miguel probably would. And he'd probably deck Ian, too, if he had to. I'll go, you keep an eye out and if things go really wrong then get help, okay?'

'Okay.'

We crept up to the edge of the grove and peered into the gloom. Victoria stayed where she was and I tip-toed as silently as I could, praying that my eyes would adjust to the darkness enough to be able to see *anything* sometime soon. Then came a flicker of light, like from a torch, and I headed in that direction and eventually heard hushed voices. I swore… they must have caught her. Oh well, nothing for it; time to take a gamble. I was quite prepared to take another beating in the process, but it was better than something really bad happening to Crystal. The light flickered again, and then illuminated a figure on the floor in a tiny clearing: Crystal, gagged and what few clothes she'd been wearing beneath her coat were mostly torn. I heard Miguel laugh.

'You got me sent down, after everything I did for you, you fucking bitch.'

There was a barely audible whimper in response, but I could just make out her face. She was crying.

''S'funny that you ended up a whore. Working for my friend, too! Stupid bitch!'

'I'll leave you to it. I should probably go find my sister and see if she knows where that prick is.' Ian's voice was startlingly close to me; I don't know how he hadn't heard me approach. He was practically on top of me, and I was between him and the playground, so he was going to find me pretty soon. I couldn't risk making any sudden movements to get out of the way. I very slowly took a few steps away from the clearing, behind a tree, and held my breath. Ian turned and walked towards my hiding place, stumbling a little in the darkness. I'm terrible at holding my breath, too. He moved practically touching my right shoulder as he fought his way through entirely the wrong way, through the tiny branches rather than the clear, soft grass path. A twig poked me in the back of the neck as he forced a branch out of his way, and I could feel myself going purple from not breathing. I prayed for the idiot to hurry up and get out of the way. Miguel had knelt beside Crystal and was saying something to her.

'You know the worst part about prison?' he asked, 'no sex. No pussy for four fucking years, can you believe it?'

I released the air slowly from my lungs and did my best to refrain from gasping. I really felt like I could do with some painkillers,my cheek seemed to be flaring up in protest, and it hurt more than it had done all day. There was a rustling, and I peered round to see Miguel fumbling with his buckle. Oh, the sick bastard was actually going to rape her. Shit, shit, shit. I had to do something drastic very quickly.

I darted out from behind the tree and charged towards him. He stood up quickly and spun round to see me dashing like a madman and pulling my arm back to take a swing at him. I could've sworn I saw him grin at me. I swung, and punched him as hard as I could on his cheek. When it connected, my knuckles instantly started to hurt. With his right hand, he grabbed me by the throat and squeezed. His left hand jabbed me in the stomach and winded me quite thoroughly.

'Look! It's your boyfriend!' the big man laughed and pushed me to the floor, where I coughed and frantically tried to get some air inside me. Then he pulled a knife out and waved it at me.

'You stupid fucking prick, you should've fucked off after the first beating. Now I'm going to fucking kill you *and* your whore girlfriend.'

He started towards me, when a gift from the heavens arrived: Victoria crashed into the little clearing and leapt at Miguel's back. She ineffectually hit the back of his head over and over, which seemed to annoy him rather than hurt him. He struggled to grab her, snarled then eventually managed to get in front of her and punch her square on the nose. Blood squirted out and she screamed as she stumbled up against a tree.

'What the fuck is wrong with this shitty fucking town?!' Miguel roared, turning back to me, 'and how many whores do you have anyway?'

I'd managed to pull myself back to my feet just in time to meet his lunge and grab his wrists, which seemed to surprise him. I caught a glimpse of Victoria, with blood pouring down her mouth and dripping from her face, and felt a huge rush of anger-inspired adrenaline. I yelled pointlessly and pushed my weight against him as much as I could, our arms outstretched Christ-like as we grappled over which one of us was going to get a knife in them. We danced like this for many seconds, and somehow we ended up with his back to Crystal, still lying on the floor. I had an idea.

I forced myself forward, pushing him closer to Crystal. He was a hell of a lot stronger than me and my arms were going numb, and my stomach was twisting and dying to empty its contents orally. One last lunge, I felt myself trying to telepathically communicate my idea over to the half-naked girl laying in the grass and dirt. I hoped she could hear it, I couldn't risk shouting out a plan so ingenious.

Crystal came through.

Miguel's grip loosened, his eyes widened and he coughed. I wrenched the knife from his hand, which had seemed to seize up in a dreadful muscular spasm, an ancient reflex built in as part of a self-destruct mechanism. I held the knife under his chin, and looked down to see Crystal's ice-white shoe thrusting up between his legs for a second time. Through her gag, she screeched as her foot met Miguel's groin again, and then again for a third strike. I moved the knife away a little, and with a whimper the big man dropped to his knees and slumped forward at my feet.

I took this opportunity to kick him in the face. I felt that he deserved that.

*   *   *

I hastily dialled 999. Victoria had passed out during the fight, with blood all over herself. Her nose was most certainly broken and she was going to need a hospital, and getting the police involved as soon as possible was probably a good idea. I had this thug unconscious and at my mercy for now, which is just where I liked him. I kicked him in the ribs whilst talking to the emergency services operator. I untied Crystal's hands, removed her gag and helped her to her feet. She was in floods of tears and she immediately wrapped her arms around me and buried her face in my chest, sobbing uncontrollably with the occasional discernable 'thank you'. I let her go, and tended to Victoria as best I could while waiting for an ambulance; I tried hard to remember anything from basic first aid training in school and placed her in something that resembled the recovery position, and wiped as much blood from her nose and mouth as I could. I sat beside her with my back against a tree, stroking her hair and listening to the sounds of the night, while my stripper friend cried quietly to herself.

A few minutes later, the sirens came.

*   *   *

I've since moved town for various reasons, and it's nice being able to feel a hell of a lot safer. I'm still learning to think of this new place as 'home', though, since all my adventures and memories, good and bad, have been locked in the same old town for years.

Although a certain someone asked if I'd give her a copy of this story as soon as I finished writing it, the problem is that she's off doing much better for herself somewhere. And since we never kept in touch, I don't know if she'll ever read this. I shouldn't have taken so long to write it, I guess.